KT-214-550

THE BIKINI PROMISE

THE BIKINI PROMISE

SHAPE UP FOR SUMMER
100 DELICIOUSLY HEALTHY RECIPES

SALLY BEE

PHOTOGRAPHY BY CLARE WINFIELD

KYLE BOOKS

THE PROMISE

THE BIKINI PROMISE. THAT'S QUITE A PROMISE, ISN'T IT?

The promise that you will get in your bikini, look good and feel confident. But it is a promise that together we can deliver. What I need you to do, besides making delicious food and enjoying your meals – probably more than you have ever done so before – is forget all the previous diets you have been on and let me guide you through my very simple, lifesaving approach to losing weight.

I am writing this Bikini Promise for you from a unique point of view. Although I have always had to keep an eye on my weight, indeed I have fluctuated up and down by nearly 13kg (2 stone) over the years, today my emphasis is always on eating for good health.

Ten years ago, completely out of the blue, I suffered three heart attacks due to a very rare heart condition that I didn't know I had. It was really tough. I had to say goodbye to my husband and my three babies as the doctors said I was going to die. My heart stopped, my eyes closed and all the pain I was suffering went away. My next breath was a miracle, and from that breath onwards I have been committed to making sure I keep my body in the best shape possible.

It's important to say that I didn't *suffer* my heart attacks because I was unfit or overweight, but I did *survive* them because I had taken good care of myself beforehand. And that is the starting point for you on this Bikini Promise journey.

There is no diet that will do what healthy eating does! Skip the diet. Eat for health.

IT'S ALL IN THE MIND

This summer, instead of feeling the usual dread when you put your jumpers in the loft and get out your summer wardrobe, you are going to have a completely different experience. You are going to get your brain in gear and start to listen to your body.

HOW ARE YOU GOING TO LOOK?

Are you a Marilyn Monroe? Or a Jane Russell? I choose these names as examples because I am a similar body shape to them. I have curvy curves, which my mum taught me to celebrate instead of be ashamed of (thank you, Mum!). So, I have an hourglass figure (curvy at the top and the bottom with a waist). You may be the same or you may be an apple shape (round) or pear shape (rounder at the bottom than the top). Whatever your body shape, I want you to know, understand and believe that it can be a beautiful body! DO NOT pay too much attention to Photoshopped images in the media. I have seen many 'beautiful' media bodies in real life, and let me tell you, they all have a bit of dimpling here and there!

So, choose someone you love the look of who has a similar shape to your own. Print out a picture of them and stick it to the fridge. You'll find it really helpful to keep your 'body goal' in mind. Start to imagine yourself in that body and how your life would be in that body shape. What clothes could you wear? How would you feel when walking into a room full of people? Would they turn their heads to look at you for all the right reasons? Would you feel proud, confident, happy, energised and beautiful? The answer is 'yes' to all of the above!

Putting yourself in the body that you deserve will make a difference to every aspect of your life. It will make you feel more confident – and confidence exudes beauty. The energy you will get from being healthier and slimmer will also be liberating.

Nothing feels or looks more beautiful than good health, and having a slim body is the best side effect of that.

When we pass a beautiful woman in the street who looks confident and elegant, most of us wish we could have what she has. But few of us ever stop to consider who decided that she was going to be one of the lucky ones. Or how much she was going to weigh. Likewise, who decides if you look good in your clothes? Who decides if you are happy? Slim? Fit? Healthy?

You are the designer of your health, your body and your destiny. Only you have the power to make the necessary changes. The starting point for this couldn't be simpler. It's all about the food that you choose to put in your body and the way that you choose to move.

Make today the day you take control. Make your Bikini Promise today.

WHAT SHOULD YOUR BIKINI BODY LOOK LIKE?

I am 5'8" tall with broad shoulders, and a curvy (UK) size 12–14. For me to get into a size 10 bikini, I would have to not only starve myself for a gazillion years, but also chop away half of my bone structure. It would be foolish of me to aim to have a body like the beautiful Elle Macpherson, who is built very differently. It's really important not to judge yourself in comparison to anyone else. This is all about you, for you and only you.

When you have a quiet moment to yourself, whip your clothes off and have a look at your body in a full-length mirror. This is the time to be honest with yourself. What you see on the outside is mirrored on the inside of your body. If you have fat sitting around your tummy, waist and back, this fat isn't only layered on the outside, it is also layered on the inside of your body, affecting all your major organs. People seem to think that when they lose weight, it comes off from the outside of their body only. This isn't true. When you lose weight and your waistline slims down, the majority of fat is lost from the inside first. With this in mind, have a good look in the mirror, jump up and down and have a wiggle about. You'll be able to see the areas where fat is sitting. These areas are likely to upset you, because you won't like the look of them. But what should worry you more is that the fat that is layered on the inside of these areas could be damaging your health.

By changing the way you eat, you will not only repair the inside of your body but at the same time lose weight. By following my principles and plan, I can promise you that you will not only achieve the best bikini body for you, you will also be in the best physical condition possible – inside and out. You will be giving yourself the opportunity to live a longer and healthier life.

So, ask yourself a few questions. I know you'll have a vision in your mind of how you'd like to look. At the same time as visualising that, ask yourself:

- Do I want to be ill or healthy?
- Which is more expensive?
- Which is more enjoyable?
- Which looks better?
- Which will make me happier?
- Which will help me live longer?

Both you and I know the answers to these questions:

- You want to be well.
- Eating for health does not cost more (my recipes prove that).
- Being healthy and slim is much more enjoyable than feeling weighed down by fat.
- We all look better when our bodies are in better shape.
- Considering all of the above, being healthier has to make me happier.
- Being healthier and slimmer cuts the risk of heart disease, stroke, certain cancers and diabetes, to name but a few.

Taking control of your weight and therefore your health is a liberating experience that proves you have control of your life. So, once you have shown that you can master an area that may well have been controlling you in the past, you can then take a look at other areas of your life that need attention without being daunted that they control you. It may be your finances, your career or your relationships. Whatever it is, just like your weight, *you* are the person that has the power to make the changes. And changing the *unsatisfactory* to the *joyous* is possible for you all.

WHY SHOULD YOU EAT FOR HEALTH?

Most diets focus on either counting calories or cutting out carbs, with weight loss as the main aim. This is the wrong way to approach losing weight. What we need to do is to focus on eating for health, then weight loss will be a very easy-to-achieve side effect.

Our bodies need certain types of food to operate properly. A bit like the engine of a high-performance car, if you put low-grade fuel into the tank, it's going to start coughing and spluttering and won't last as long, even if initially there are no problems. Similarly, there are many foods that give the impression of being good for us, but actually by eating them we are damaging our 'engine' and potentially shortening its lifespan.

THE BASIC PRINCIPLES OF EATING FOR HEALTH

The very first thing to do is cut out all chemicals and processed food from your life. This might include items that you would assume are good for you, such as pre-prepared food that has the word 'diet' written on the packet. Also, carefully read labels that say 'low fat', in particular yogurts and desserts. These are often very high in sugar, which then turns into fat in the body. Remember that even though a ready meal may say on the packet that it's low in fat, sugar and salt, the very fact that it is pre-packed will mean that it's been through a process that takes much of the goodness out of the ingredients. So, although

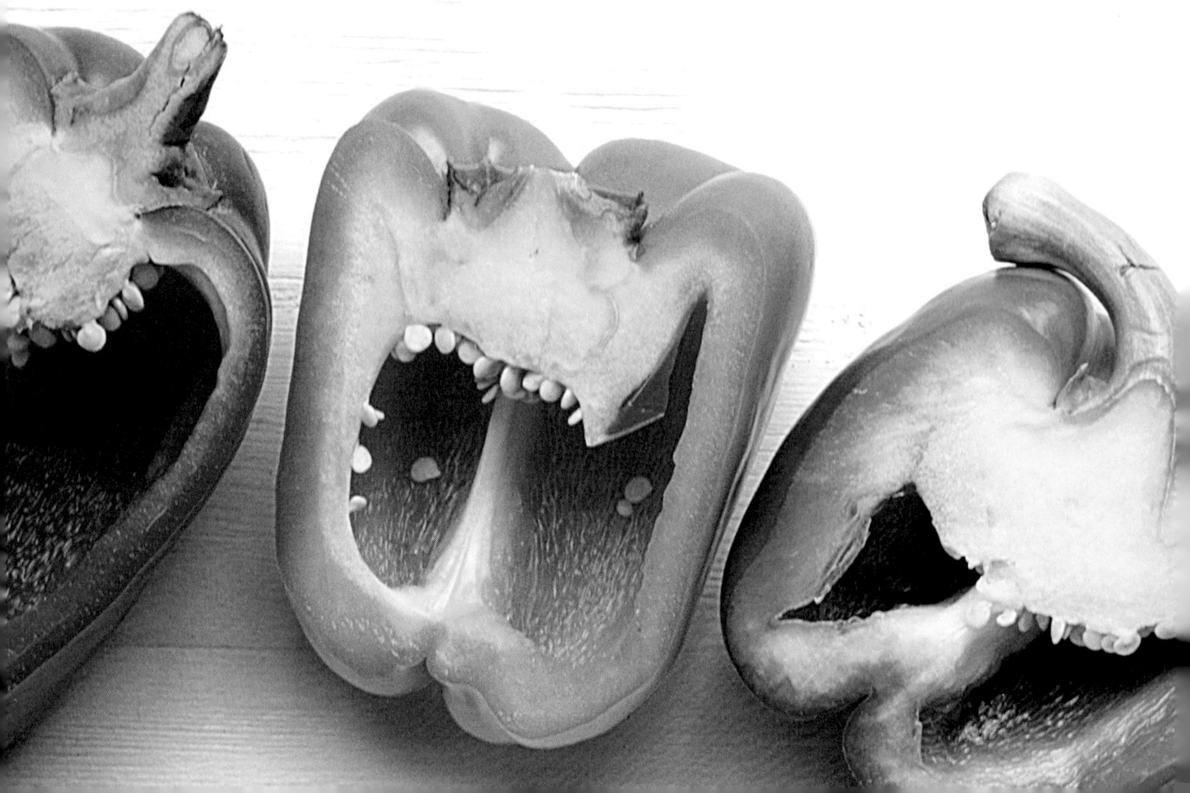

you may not be putting any of the real nasties into your body, you are not giving your body many of the nutrients that it needs to thrive. These are the lifesaving healthy elements that are found in fresh, unprocessed food.

You are going to start 'clean eating', in other words eating fresh, largely unprocessed food in its most natural form. That's not to say this is an eating plan filled with mung beans and spinach; when you look at the recipes you'll see they are all recognisable family favourites that will feed your soul as well as your body. And although I encourage you to avoid processed foods that have the words 'low fat' or 'diet', there are a few exceptions. I do use 'low-fat' dairy products in my recipes, such as low-fat crème fraîche and low-fat natural Greek yogurt, but I never use anything that has added sugar or chemicals. Don't worry, it's all really easy to follow.

The Bikini Promise is about what you MUST eat rather than what you must not!

SIX STEPS TO STAY ON TRACK

Below are my six steps to help you stay on track. Print them out and pop them on your fridge, next to your bed, or on your desk. Actually, put copies everywhere you spend time, to help keep you focused.

STEP 1
GET YOUR BRAIN IN GEAR!

From this moment forward I want you to imagine you already have your dream bikini body. Look at the picture you have chosen and stuck up on the fridge. Start behaving, thinking, feeling and acting like you are already in this body. What would this person eat? How would they eat? How much would they eat?

Believe that you can break free from eating patterns you may have inherited. Understand that committing to your Bikini Promise isn't about affordability, or having the time, or waiting until you can join the gym. Committing to your Bikini Promise starts right now with changing the way you view yourself, and changing the way you think about what you eat and how you move. Master this and your life, along with your bikini size, will change forever.

STEP 2
WHY ARE YOU EATING?

Every time you are about to put food in your mouth ask yourself are you 'tummy' hungry or 'brain' hungry? If you feel hungry but had a large meal an hour or so ago, your stomach isn't empty and asking for food. In this situation, it is probably your brain telling you to eat because your blood sugar levels have dropped. So instead of eating too much food, just eat a small palmful of nuts and raisins (see page 29 for other snack ideas). This will be enough to lift your blood sugar levels and keep you going until you are properly 'tummy' hungry.

STEP 3
NEED OR GREED?

Every time you are about to put food in your mouth, ask yourself, is it 'need?' or 'greed'? If you haven't eaten for three or four hours and feel hungry, you know this is a 'need' meal and you require something nutritious to fuel your body. This is the time to choose one of the delicious full meal recipes from the plan and sit down to eat properly.

If, however, you have had breakfast and then met friends for coffee and cake an hour later, this isn't a 'need' meal – it is a 'greed' meal. When you are in the process of getting healthy and losing weight, try not to put yourself in the position of eating a 'greed' meal – or at least wait for a special occasion to enjoy a special and worthwhile treat.

STEP 4
GET PREPARED TO MEAL MATCH

Every time you are about to put food in your mouth ask yourself, can I do a better meal match? By this I mean matching the food you eat to your daily activities. For example, if I am sitting at my desk writing, I don't need lots of spare energy, but I do still need lots of good nutrients to keep my brain sharp. A full eight hours writing a day is not physically draining but it sure makes my brain hurt! In this case I would go for a light breakfast and lunch, consisting of fish or chicken with a delicious salad (no soggy lettuce leaves in sight!), or some roasted vegetables. This would nourish me but not make me sleepy during the afternoon when I've got my editor breathing down my neck wanting finished copy. I would then probably only need another light meal at around 6pm, as sitting all day at a desk doesn't use many calories.

If, on the other hand, I am having a busy week, rushing around from one event to another, needing lots more energy to keep me active throughout the day, I would opt for a more substantial breakfast that would keep me going for longer. I would make sure I had plenty of nuts, raisins and fruit in my bag for on-the-go snacks and I would try and make time for a more substantial lunch. This is especially important if I thought I wouldn't get an evening meal at a decent time.

To help you meal match, each dish has been labelled **LIGHT** or **ACTIVE**. **LIGHT** dishes are for when you need slightly less energy, for instance if you are going to be sitting at your desk. **ACTIVE** dishes are a little more energy dense and so perfect for when you are physically busy. Please don't think that one is better than the other; they are both developed with good health and weight loss in mind. If you are having a 'usual' activity day for you, you will need two **LIGHT** meals and one **ACTIVE** meal. Obviously, if you are more active than usual, then it's perfectly fine to have one **LIGHT** meal and two **ACTIVE**.

Remember this is your Bikini Promise and you have to make it work for you! I can't sit on your shoulder and tell you what you should choose to eat at every mealtime, so keep reminding yourself why you started this in the first place. Look at your aim photograph and keep focused on being as healthy as possible, which will, of course, help you be as slim as is perfect for you.

STEP 5
HOVER YOUR HAND!

Every time you make a meal, hover your hand over your plate first. We are all different shapes and sizes. It would be foolish for me to give a 6ft rugby player the same diet plan as a 4ft ballerina! This is why you need to gauge your portion size. My rule is that when losing weight, the protein and carbohydrate in any meal need to be no larger on the plate than the size of your hovered hand.

We have all lost sight of what a normal portion is these days – the fact is, we are becoming an obese nation because we simply eat too much and move too little. So, from now on, your portion size has to be the size of your flat hand with your fingers together. Simply hover your hand over your plate of food and you will quickly get the measure of how much you are overeating. The only food that is allowed outside of your hand is salad, vegetables or fruit.

Portion size is an area where many, many people go wrong. You may be eating all the right healthy foods, but if you eat too much of them, you will gain weight.

STEP 6
NO LATE NIGHT-TIME MEALS

Do you wake up feeling tired in the mornings? Is your mouth sometimes terribly dry first thing? Are your eyes puffy? Eating late at night causes many of these symptoms: the food remains in your stomach and the digestion process takes place while your body is supposed to be resting. Because you are not moving around, the requirements for food and energy are minimal, so the food you have eaten before bed is not utilised.

Your body needs a 12-hour break without food, so that your digestion system gets a rest along with everything else. Unused food in your stomach at night can turn toxic. So if you have breakfast at 7.30am, don't eat your last meal any later than 7.30pm the night before. This will not only aid your weight loss but you'll wake up with better skin, clearer eyes and no dry mouth or sore throat.

If you are not used to this, you might not like going to bed feeling hungry. But get through the first week and you will get to love what I now regard as the slim-in-the-morning feeling rather than a hungry one! It's also a great way to get good sleep, as your whole system gets to rest properly without having to digest food when you are sleeping. If you are used to snacking in the evening, make sure you have an active day so you are worn out and get an early night, killing two birds with one stone. No naughty night-time eating and a great night's sleep. Wow, you will wake up slimmer and more radiant after a good 10 hours! Well done!

START A DIARY

Have you ever suffered from food amnesia? You weigh yourself at the end of the week and wonder why you have piled on another 1.5kg (3.3lb) when you've been 'so good'! Well, this isn't down to heavy bones or slow metabolism; this is simply down to eating more than your body needs. It's all too easy to have the odd biscuit, packet of crisps or cake and then conveniently forget that you ate them.

On the Bikini Promise this shouldn't happen. But just in case you have some naughty habits that need addressing, I want you to keep an honest food diary for a week. Write down EVERYTHING that passes your lips. Every drink, every sweetie, every meal, EVERYTHING!

Keeping a diary will help you stop and think before you eat something, and gives you time to think back over your six steps. Looking back at your diary you will be able to see any empty calories that are sitting there just waiting to dive onto your hips!

If you write down the times you eat, you will also be able to see *when* you crave sweet things, which will help you to prepare for and beat 'greed' hunger. So, if every afternoon at 3pm you have written down that you eat a couple of biscuits, this should tell you that your sugar levels drop at this time. The way to avoid that is either to have a more substantial lunch that will see you through to dinner, or to make sure that at 2.30pm you pre-empt that sugar drop by having a small handful of nuts and raisins. These will offer a heath benefit and lift your sugar levels sufficiently to take away your cravings. Bingo!

STILL ENJOY TREATS!

Writing a food diary inevitably leads to thoughts about the treats that you love and are going to miss. This is a really important point that shouldn't be ignored. As a surviving heart patient, I know what is important in life: Love. Family. Friends. Chocolate!

The point is, we all love treats; they are part of life, and that's okay. What is not okay is to have them every day, or to have them in place of a healthy meal. So if you are out with friends, celebrating a birthday or whatever it may be, don't feel that you have to say 'no' to everything. You have my absolute blessing to enjoy special treats every now and then. But just remember that having one slice/piece doesn't mean you have fallen off the wagon and that you may as well eat the whole plate/ box! All it means is that you need to take it easy on the food front the following day and cut your portion size accordingly. An extra walk or a little more exercise the next day will also alleviate any guilt.

Life is short, and treats are essential, just be sensible and keep your healthy eating in mind.

EXERCISE – YOUR SECRET WEAPON!

ACTIVE LIVING EXERCISE LEVEL 1

If exercise was a pill, it would be one of the most cost-effective drugs ever invented. The health benefits of exercise are amazing and being fit on the inside helps us look better on the outside. Win, win!

Having a chronic illness or growing older can make an active lifestyle seem unachievable. And being too busy looking after children, working or not being able to afford gym memberships are all excuses used for not exercising. But if we change the word exercise to 'movement' or 'active living', you should feel encouraged that you can also participate in a way that fits and suits you.

If you don't currently do any exercise, pay particular attention to the Active Living section in preparation for Proactive Exercise. The Active Living section should be done for a week before leading onto Proactive Exercise. You can and must continue with the principles of Active Living throughout your life, but you will also need to up the exercise stakes during your Bikini Promise to get the best results.

Once you get started with Active Living, you will feel and see the rewards so quickly that you'll want to do more and more. Active Living and movement is a healthy and achievable way to move onto more vigorous exercise. And once you get onto your full-on exercise stage, you'll find it addictive. When you exercise, your brain releases feel-good hormones that keep you going back for more and, of course, the more you move, the more calories you will burn and the more weight you'll lose. Movement and exercise will also firm up your wobbly bits, which is a big worry for most of us before getting into our bikini!

As I've already said, losing weight is about stopping bad habits, eating healthily, in the appropriate portion size, and moving more.

To begin moving more, you have to start by becoming more aware of what your body is doing. This is another element that is all about you. Do not compare yourself to anyone else at this point; we are all different with different abilities, so just concentrate on lovely you.

So, when you are walking through town doing your shopping, could you walk any quicker? Instead of doing the supermarket shopping in 60 minutes, could you do it in half the time? Could you stand up any taller and push your shoulders back and hold your tummy tighter? Could you swing your arms more as you walk and put a little bounce in your step? I'll bet the answer to these questions is 'yes'. When you are becoming more aware of your body, you'll very quickly realise that there is always more you could be doing to get your body moving.

With that in mind – and although these instructions might seem very simple – please do engage in them fully to ease you into the next exercise level.

10 WAYS TO START ACTIVE LIVING

In the morning, before getting up, wake your muscles up by tensing and relaxing all of them from your toes up to your neck, all at the same time, ten times. Not only will this help to get the blood and oxygen moving around your body, but it will also alert you to any aches and pains that you want to be careful of during the day's activities.

Incorporating exercise into your daily routine may take a little getting used to, but once you set your mind to it, you'll soon realise how easy it is to incorporate exercise into just about everything you do. For example:

1. When you are walking around town, shopping and running errands, get a wiggle on and walk much quicker. Hold your tummy tight and your shoulders back.

2. Always take the stairs, never the lift.

3. Instead of sitting to talk on the phone, stand up and walk around.

4. Go for a walk in your lunch break.

5. If it takes you 60 minutes to do the supermarket shopping, try to do it in half the time.

6. Get off your bus two stops earlier and walk the rest of the way.

7. When you are sitting at your desk, sit up straight, pull your tummy muscles in and keep your shoulders back. Don't slump!

8. Walk instead of drive, whenever possible.

9. Try placing your computer on a platform of books or a solid box on your desk so that you stand to type instead of sit. This can burn as many as 500 extra calories a day!

10. Try to be mindful of movement at all times. Changing the way you do two normal daytime activities over the space of a month can burn the equivalent amount of calories to doing a 120-mile walk, so it is certainly not to be sniffed at!

Sit and think about what other everyday activities you could do to increase your movement. I completely understand that some people have medical barriers that stop them from exercising. I'm not allowed to do any heavy lifting and I can't let my heart rate get too high, so this rules out very strenuous cardio exercise for me, but there is plenty that I *can* do.

Tasks such as changing bed linen, vacuuming, dusting to music and other household jobs are excellent exercises. Set yourself time limits or deadlines to finish by. This is all brilliant for me because these are all jobs that I hate doing, but when I attack them like an exercise class not only do I get them done much quicker, but I feel they have also been completely worthwhile because I've been slimming my waistline at the same time!

Gardening presents a multitude of ways to exercise and DIY and maintenance jobs use energy and stretch muscles not normally used.

When you arrive at work or any other destination, continue your challenge to keep moving by finding ways to exercise that fit in with your day's objectives.

If you work in an office, go and visit a colleague to discuss a point rather than phoning them. As long as you aren't 100 floors up, try to take the stairs instead of the lift. Try to get out for a 10-minute walk at lunchtime. When you need the bathroom – don't use the nearest one – walk that little bit further. While doing all of this, don't tell your boss it is Sally Bee's fault that you are never at your desk!

Hobbies can present you with excellent ways to increase movement and exercise. Apart from the obvious sports, other activities are also perfect to get your heart pumping. Dancing burns calories at a fast rate and is a fun way to exercise. Swimming, Pilates, yoga and tai chi are all great ways to enjoy exercise. If you have an active sex life, this is one of the most fun ways to get good exercise. Yes really! Making love burns almost as many calories as a 30-minute jog and is much more fun.

When I was in hospital recovering from my heart attacks, I was given a leaflet to read about what I could and couldn't do when I got home. It told me I could do light housework, smooth down the bed covers and resume sexual relations as this was no more strenuous than watching a good comedy on TV. It actually said that! Let's just say that, if you enjoy fun with your partner, this too is exercise of the best kind. Being happy and relaxed is very good for heart health, so let those endorphins do their best.

PRO-ACTIVE EXERCISE LEVEL 2

So, after a week of Active Living, getting used to exercise level 1, it's time to get moving more and being pro-active with your exercise. It's time to move along to the Pro-active Level.

Pro-active Exercise is exercise that gets your heart pumping, your body moving and sweating and your calories burning for at least 30 minutes, three times a week.

If you are already enjoying Pro-active Exercise, that's fantastic. As you have now made the Bikini Promise, exercise is going to become your second best friend (your first best friend is always good food!), so it is still worth revisiting your exercise plan and seeing if there is anything more effective you can be doing in the time you have available.

When you begin any new strenuous exercise regime after a period of inactivity, get a check-up from your doctor if:

• You've been diagnosed with heart problems, high blood pressure or other medical conditions.

• You've been sedentary for over a year.

• If you're over 65 and don't currently exercise.

• You're pregnant.

• You have diabetes.

• You've ever experienced chest pains, dizziness or fainting spells.

• You're recovering from an injury or illness.

• You have a diagnosed medical condition or illness.

Use your best judgment and see your doctor if you have any questions about what you should be doing. Even if you don't have any problems, you may want to get a full check-up before you start exercising, especially if it's been a long time since you last worked out.

WHAT TO WEAR?

You don't want any barriers getting in the way of your new bikini body, so when dressing to exercise, **think comfort**. Shorts, T-shirts, leggings... There's no right and wrong when it comes to exercise clothes. It's whatever makes you feel good and keeps you comfortable. Test your clothes before you go to the gym or for a walk, to make sure they don't chafe, ride up, slide down or show more than you want! You may also want to invest in clothes made of special materials that keep you cool and dry in the summer and warm in the winter. Fancy fabrics aren't essential, but they do make workouts more comfortable.

Protect yourself. Wear light-coloured clothes, a hat, plenty of sunscreen and sunglasses if you're exercising outdoors.

Wear the right shoes for your activity. For weight training and low-impact activities, consider a cross-training shoe, running or walking shoes. If you're going to be running, you'll want running shoes that give your feet plenty of support. Similarly, if you're participating in a sport such as basketball or football, you'll want sport-specific shoes so you don't hurt yourself. But remember, just walking quicker won't cost you anything and as long as you're not wearing high heels, and your shoes are comfortable, anything goes! And be picky about your workout socks – if they're too thick or thin you could get blisters, which will ruin a good workout.

Lastly, **be safe**. Make sure your clothes and shoes have reflective material on them if you're out and about at night.

THERE IS SO MUCH CHOICE!

There certainly is. At my local leisure centre alone there is:

Body combat
Spin (group cycling)
Step
Martial arts
HIIT (High Intensity Interval Training)
Walking club
Aqua aerobics
Body pump
LBT (legs, bums and tums)
Body balance
Dynamic yoga
Pilates
Pure abs
Zumba
Hula hooping

I find that going to a class is the most motivating way to exercise, and I love classes with lots of loud music. Zumba is one of my favourites, as I get lost in the music and dance like a nutter for an hour. Where else, at the age of 47, would I be able to bounce around and wave my arms in the air and dance like I just don't care and nobody bats an eyelid! It's fabulous and I love it.

When you are looking for a class, make sure you find one that fits in with your schedule. Most leisure centres have classes throughout the whole day and evening so you can definitely find one that suits. Get your friends signed up too, then you can encourage each other. Remember, no matter how much you are dreading a class before you go and feeling like you don't have the energy, you will NEVER regret going and will ALWAYS feel better afterwards.

I find that exercising in the evening really helps with **Step 6 – No late night-time meals** (see page 17). After a vigorous exercise class, you will find that you cannot eat a big meal, but you'll need plenty of water to drink. So on these nights, an energetic class, no big meal in the evening after the class, lots of water to drink and an early night will bring a massive boost to your weight loss!

EXERCISING AT HOME

I have to be honest and say that you have to be very motivated to exercise at home, but if you can commit it's a brilliant way to exercise as you can do it when it suits you, and it's free!

I have a collection of fitness DVDs at home and, when the house is quiet, I will pop one on and jump around for 30 minutes. It's great fun, totally liberating, albeit a little bit embarrassing if the window cleaner turns up!

My advice is change-it-up regularly so that you don't get bored. Try lots of different activities and classes. When I am working away from home, I always Google the nearest leisure centre and the classes they have available so I can use that time away from home to squeeze in a quick class. It's never a problem that I don't know anyone – people that go to exercise classes are generally very friendly!

TIPS FOR SUCCESSFUL EXERCISE

As with everything else on the Bikini Promise, the principle is simple.

Pace yourself. Overdoing it is just as bad as under-doing it! Don't try to be superhuman, but don't be afraid to try things if you feel ready. Use your common sense. Give an activity a try: if you can do it easily, you can push yourself further the next time.

It doesn't matter what type of exercise you are doing, whether you are using rubber bands, bicycles or Pilates machines, all that matters is that you make your muscles work hard and get your heart rate up for at least 30 minutes, three times a week. After that, how you do it is completely up to you and your imagination. Enjoy!

GET ORGANISED

So, you have sorted out your goal, you have a beautiful picture on the fridge that is going to help you reach your goal. You have committed to Active Living and beyond. Now let's have a quick chat about food.

If you are overweight it is because you eat too much of the wrong types of food and you don't move enough. Sounds simple to rectify doesn't it? However, we all know it isn't simple to rectify and that is why you have probably tried just about every diet going over the years. The fact that you are reading my book tells me that your previous diets haven't worked, or at least not in the long term.

Let me explain how the Bikini Promise is different:

This is not a plan where I tell you exactly what you must eat for today's breakfast, lunch and dinner. How do I know what activities you are doing today? How do I know if your hormones are ruling you, or if you have a bunch of meetings so will be snacking? How will I know if you are upset, happy, angry... in other words, being emotional with your choices of food.

The fact is that although I like to consider myself a little magical, I can't walk in your shoes every day, I can only walk in mine.

The Bikini Promise is all about giving you the tools to make healthy decisions. It's about giving you the information (the recipes) that will support your healthy eating decisions. It's about educating you and sharing with you the hints and tips that will get you over tricky moments, help you stop and think about what you are doing to your body and to your future health. The Bikini Promise is all about *YOU* taking control of *your* life, and that will result in a healthier, happier and slimmer YOU!

No matter how slow you go, you are still lapping everyone sitting on the couch!

The safety rule is you should be able to hold a conversation while exercising but not be able to sing a song!

YOUR SHOPPING LIST

Below is a list of storecupboard ingredients that are great to have to hand. It's a good idea to build up a collection of herbs and spices, which will come in useful again and again (you probably have many of them already).

Dried rosemary
Dried oregano
Dried basil
Dried Italian herbs
Black peppercorns
Dried chilli flakes
Ground cumin
Cajun spice mix
Curry powder
Garam masala
Garlic granules
Celery salt
Smoked paprika
Ground ginger
Ground coriander
Worcestershire sauce
Teriyaki sauce
Soy sauce
Runny honey
Wholegrain mustard
English mustard powder
Curry paste
Tomato purée
Balsamic vinegar
White wine vinegar
Canned kidney beans
Red and green lentils (including Puy lentils)
Wholemeal pasta
Brown rice
Basmati rice

Also, buy some low-salt stock cubes. You can buy lovely fresh stock, or make your own, but I'm going to assume that you are as busy as I am, and simply don't have the time!

TOMATOES

However you eat tomatoes, be it canned, puréed, fresh, cooked, roasted or in tomato sauce, they will be building up your natural immunity AND they are low in fat and taste gorgeous. So stock up on:

Canned chopped tomatoes
Tomato passata
Tomato purée

OILS

Almost all of my savoury dishes use extra virgin olive oil. Olive oil is proven to be good for you, and to lower blood cholesterol. It's particularly good when heated with onions and garlic: the combination of flavours makes a great base for a dish – you'll notice that the majority of my savoury dishes start with these three ingredients.

'Extra virgin' means the first, most wholesome press of the olives, which in turn means it contains more goodness. The darker green the colour, the healthier and tastier the olive oil.

Light olive oil does not mean it's lower in calories, as some people assume. Light olive oil is paler than extra virgin olive oil, and has a milder flavour, as it is taken from a much later press of the olives. Because it doesn't have such a strong flavour, it is perfect to use in desserts and some salad dressings. I suggest you buy a large bottle of extra virgin olive oil and a small bottle of light olive oil.

I also use **sesame oil** when stir-frying in a wok, as it has a much higher burn temperature than olive oil so doesn't get as smoky! A small bottle will last you ages.

A note on frozen vegetables

If you are going to spend money on food for the freezer, don't spend it on ready-made meals. Instead, buy frozen vegetables, fruit and herbs that will make life easier but still be good for your health!

FREEZER INGREDIENTS

You are not going to be eating ready meals, so instead I suggest you fill your freezer up with the following:

Chopped onions
Sliced peppers
Sliced mushrooms
Peas
Spinach
Sweetcorn
Mixed vegetables

So that you always have fresh chilli to hand, buy a packet of fresh red and green chillies, wash, dry and cut them into halves and pop them in a bag in the freezer. Then, when a recipe calls for some chilli, you can quickly defrost what you need, when you need it!

Bread

Throughout the book you will see I mention *whole-nutty bread*. That is my term for any bread that is made of wholegrain with nuts in it. If a recipe calls for whole-nutty bread, one portion is one slice.

Dairy

Low-fat dairy products such as crème fraîche and Greek yogurt are wonderful to use, but please avoid anything with extra sweeteners or anything that says 'diet' on the label. Keep it natural and if you need a little sweetness then add fruit or a drop of honey.

Butter

Because the Bikini Promise is a commitment to chemical-free, clean eating, I recommend serving proper butter instead of margarines or spreads. Having said that, I know there are some good products on the market that are proven to lower cholesterol, so this is entirely up to you. I like the taste of butter and only ever have a tiny splodge... but enjoy it. Remember, healthy eating has to be sustainable for life!

STARTING THE DAY THE RIGHT WAY!

A good breakfast is really important when you've made your Bikini Promise. You will have come to the end of your 12-hour fast, so what you eat for breakfast will determine how you feel all day! So, besides the yummy delights in the *Ten Ways with Eggs* chapter (page 130), here are a few extra breakfast ideas:

Low-fat Greek yogurt with Fruit Compote
(see page 182)

Porridge oats with Fruit Compote
Cook 25g instant porridge oats in 150ml skimmed milk. Serve with 2 tablespoons of fruit compote.

Quinoa porridge with Fruit Compote
Cook 2 tablespoons of quinoa according to the packet instructions and add a pinch of cinnamon. Add 2 tablespoons of low-fat, natural Greek yogurt and 2 tablespoons of fruit compote.

Kippers with mushrooms
Grill a kipper fillet for 5 minutes on each side, then add six sliced mushrooms for the final 5 minutes. Serve with 1 small wholemeal pitta bread and lemon wedges.

Peanut butter oatcakes
Spread two oatcakes with unsweetened peanut butter and half a banana, mashed.

Wholegrain bagel and cream cheese with a side of strawberries

2 crumpets with Marmite

Fresh fruit salad with two oatcakes

Bacon and tomato open sandwich
Grill two lean rashers of bacon and grill two large tomatoes. Serve on whole-nutty toast.

Avocado on whole-nutty toast with 1 hard-boiled egg

Mushrooms and spinach on toast
Slice and season six mushrooms and grill. Melt a small knob of butter in a pan, add the mushrooms and juices, add a handful of spinach and cook until wilted. Serve on 1 slice of whole-nutty toast.

Toasted wholemeal bagel with low-sugar jam

Orange and mint salad
Mix 1 segmented orange with three chopped dates, 1 tablespoon of chopped walnuts and some torn mint leaves.

Make sure EVERYTHING you eat offers your body a healthy benefit.

SNACKS

You can have up to three snacks a day, but remember to listen to your body to work out what it needs. Need or Greed?

Snacks should be small bundles of nutrition.

- One piece of fruit or a palmful of small fruit (such as grapes or strawberries)
- Nuts and raisins (an egg-cup full is plenty)
- Blanched whole almonds (an egg-cup full)
- Soft figs (an egg-cup full)
- Brazil nuts (an egg-cup full)
- Sunflower and pumpkin seeds (an egg-cup full)
- Dried cranberries (an egg-cup full)
- Soft dried fruit (an egg-cup full)
- Soft dried dates (an egg-cup full)
- 5 dried apricots
- Pomegranate seeds (an egg-cup full)

Remember – if it has no health benefit – don't eat it!

SALADS SOUPS AND SIDES

ACTIVE

MINTY ROCKET, TUNA & PASTA SALAD

SERVES 4

320g wholewheat penne (or other similar shaped pasta)
150g frozen sweetcorn kernels
160g can tuna in spring water, drained
60g rocket leaves
a large handful of green olives, pitted and quartered
grated zest and juice of 1 unwaxed lemon
a handful of fresh mint leaves, chopped
freshly ground black pepper, to taste
1 tablespoon extra virgin olive oil

This recipe makes a lovely big bowl of healthy pasta salad, bursting with herby goodness, and it can be made in a matter of minutes. Serve at the table, or pop into lunchboxes or picnic hampers. 75g of dried pasta is a perfect portion size for one person.

1. Cook the pasta in boiling water according to the packet instructions, then 3 minutes before the end of the cooking time, add the sweetcorn.

2. Once the pasta and sweetcorn are cooked, drain, run under cold water and transfer to a large bowl.

3. Add all the remaining ingredients, mix to combine and serve.

Cut out all chemicals! Go natural, natural, natural!

V

ROASTED RED PEPPER SOUP WITH SPINACH

SERVES 4–6

- 1 large butternut squash, peeled, deseeded and cut into 1cm chunks
- 3 red peppers, deseeded and diced
- 6 tomatoes, cut into wedges
- 4 garlic cloves, peeled and crushed
- 2 tablespoons extra virgin olive oil
- 1 teaspoon smoked paprika
- freshly ground black pepper, to taste
- 750ml low-salt vegetable stock
- 1 tablespoon tomato purée
- 100g baby leaf spinach

Oh my goodness, such a luxuriously rich flavour in such a simple and healthy soup!

1. Preheat the oven to 180°C/gas mark 4.

2. Place the butternut squash, peppers, tomatoes and garlic into a large flameproof, lidded casserole. Drizzle with the olive oil and sprinkle over the paprika and plenty of black pepper. Place the lid on the dish and transfer to the oven for about 20 minutes, then remove the lid and return to the oven for a further 20 minutes, until all the vegetables are soft and beginning to caramelise.

3. Place the dish on the hob and use a handheld stick blender or potato masher to break the vegetables down to a chunky texture (you want to retain some lumps). Add the stock and the tomato purée and bring to the boil, then turn the heat down and simmer gently for 5 minutes.

4. Just before serving, stir in the spinach leaves and allow them to wilt down for a minute or so. Ladle the soup into bowls and serve immediately.

LIGHT

WARM SALMON SALAD WITH AVOCADO

SERVES 2

2 skinless and boneless salmon fillets
12 cherry tomatoes
1 tablespoon runny honey
1 tablespoon soy sauce
1 teaspoon garlic granules

FOR THE SALAD:
1 avocado, halved, pitted, peeled and cubed
½ cucumber, cubed
2 little gem lettuces, shredded
handful of chopped chives, parsley or dill

Salmon and avocado do not only taste great together, they also work brilliantly nutritionally. Avocado is nutrient dense and is wonderful for lowering blood cholesterol. Salmon is high in protein and omega-3 fatty acids.

1. Preheat the oven to 200°C/gas mark 6.

2. Take two large pieces of baking parchment, and layer them to make a double-thickness parcel, big enough to house the salmon. Place the salmon fillets on the centre of the baking parchment, then pop the cherry tomatoes, honey, soy sauce and garlic granules on top. Seal up the parcel, leaving some space inside it to allow the hot air to circulate.

3. Pop the salmon parcel on a baking tray and bake for 18–20 minutes, depending on the thickness of the fillets. (You know when salmon is cooked when the flesh is opaque throughout.)

4. Meanwhile, mix the avocado and cucumber with the shredded lettuce and chopped herbs. Divide the salad between two plates.

5. Once the salmon and tomatoes are cooked, remove them from the oven and place them on top of the salad, pouring over the warm, delicious juices from the parcel.

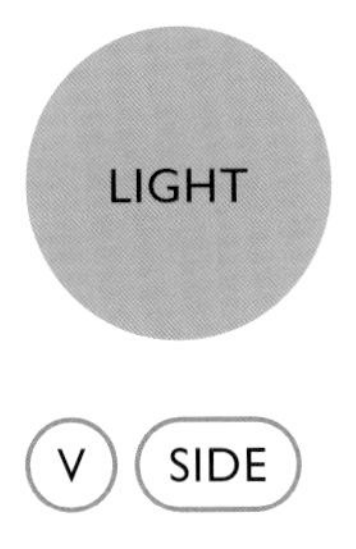

V SIDE

SALLY BEE'S MEGA NUTRI MIX ON THE SIDE

SERVES 4

- 2 tablespoons extra virgin olive oil, plus extra for drizzling
- 2 spring onions, finely sliced
- 1 leek, washed, trimmed and thinly sliced
- 1 green chilli, deseeded and finely chopped
- 1 courgette, washed and cut into strips lengthwise with a peeler
- 2 garlic cloves, peeled and crushed
- 150g tenderstem broccoli
- 100g frozen sweetcorn kernels
- 150g spinach
- 400ml low-salt vegetable stock
- 200g cooked brown rice or bulgar wheat
- 2 sprigs of lemon thyme, leaves removed and chopped (discard stalks)
- 1 teaspoon capers (optional)
- freshly ground black pepper, to taste
- a handful of fresh mint leaves, chopped
- grated zest and juice of 2 limes or 1 unwaxed lemon

Oh my goodness, this is the BEST side dish ever! I call it a side dish, though I often eat it as a main course, a lunch, a supper, or as a snack… I basically just eat it at every opportunity. You'll love it, too. If you want to turn it into a main course, you'll need to add some protein. So serve it with either chicken, fish or an egg-cup full of walnuts (which also contain brilliant omega-3).

1. Heat the olive oil in a large non-stick, lidded saucepan, then add the spring onions, leek, green chilli, courgette strips and garlic. Cook for 4 minutes, stirring, until all the vegetables are starting to soften.

2. Add the broccoli, sweetcorn, spinach and stock. Bring to the boil, then reduce the heat and simmer gently for 5 minutes. At this stage, if you have a food-processor or handheld stick blender, remove half of the mixture and blend it into a smooth sauce, then add it back to the pan. (You can leave this stage out if you prefer – it'll still be as gorgeous and good for you but slightly less creamy.)

3. Finally, add the cooked rice or bulgar wheat, lemon thyme, capers (if using) and season well with black pepper. Stir in the mint and lime or lemon juice and zest, add a little drizzle of olive oil and serve. The dish will keep well for up to 4 days in the fridge.

TIP: A jar of capers is a wonderful thing to have to hand in the fridge. They add a delicious sharpness to any dish, which will help if you are leaving out salt. If you've never tried them before, give them a go!

LIGHT

V

CARROT SOUP WITH GINGER & CHILLI

SERVES 4–6

2 tablespoons extra virgin olive oil
1 large onion, peeled and chopped
3cm piece of fresh root ginger, peeled and finely chopped
1 red chilli, deseeded and finely chopped
1 leek, washed, trimmed and chopped
1 celery stick, chopped
2 garlic cloves, peeled and crushed
1kg carrots, peeled and finely chopped
1.5 litres low-salt vegetable stock
4 tablespoons low-fat crème fraîche

A traditional, nutritious soup with a spicy twist!

1. Heat the oil in a large non-stick saucepan over a medium heat and add the onion, ginger and chilli. Cook for 3–4 minutes, stirring, until the onion is soft and transparent.

2. Add the leek, celery, garlic and carrots, then pour in the stock. Bring to the boil, then cover and simmer for 20–25 minutes, until the carrots are soft.

3. Blitz with a handheld stick blender or whiz in a liquidiser, then pour into bowls, swirling in a spoon of crème fraîche just before serving.

Are you 'tummy' hungry or 'brain' hungry? If you feel hungry but have had a large meal an hour or so ago, your stomach isn't empty and asking for food.

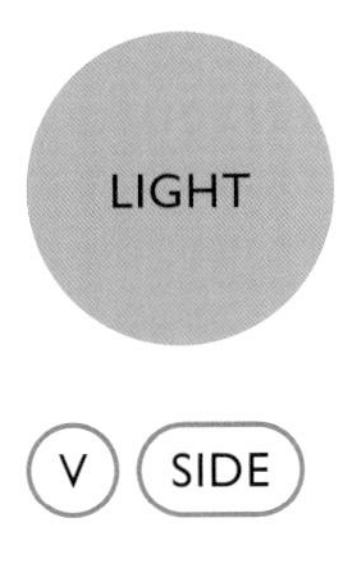

COCONUT, RICE & LENTIL SALAD

V SIDE

SERVES 4

- 2 tablespoons extra virgin olive oil
- 1 large onion, peeled and finely chopped
- 2 bay leaves
- 1 cinnamon stick
- 1 star anise
- 175g green lentils, uncooked
- 175g red lentils, uncooked
- 175g brown basmati rice
- 30g desiccated coconut
- 1.7 litres low-salt vegetable stock
- freshly ground black pepper, to taste
- a handful of fresh coriander or parsley, chopped
- a handful of pecan nuts, chopped (or unsalted, unroasted nuts of your choice)

This dish is brilliant to take to work in a lunchbox, or use as a 'bed' for a chicken or fish dish.

1. Heat the oil in a large saucepan over a medium heat and fry the onion with the bay leaves, cinnamon stick and star anise, stirring, until the onions are golden brown.

2. Stir in the green lentils, red lentils, rice and coconut, then add the vegetable stock. Bring to the boil and cover, then simmer gently for about 20–30 minutes or until the rice and lentils are just cooked but still firm. Drain and rinse under the cold tap, then leave to drain again in a colander until cold.

3. Stir and season with plenty of black pepper, then add the fresh herbs and chopped pecan nuts, to serve.

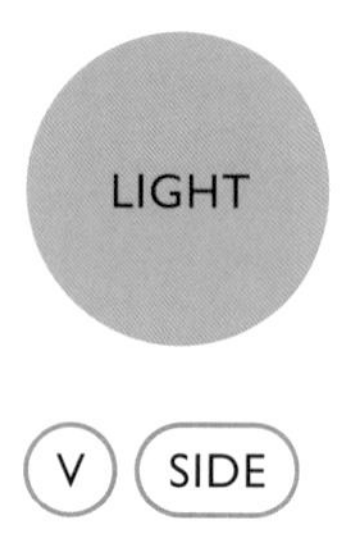

RED CABBAGE WITH APPLE

(V) (SIDE)

SERVES 4–6

- I tablespoon extra virgin olive oil
- I onion, peeled and finely chopped
- 500g red cabbage, tough stem removed, leaves shredded
- I large eating apple, peeled, cored and chopped
- 2 bay leaves
- I teaspoon ground cinnamon
- I star anise
- I25ml grape juice
- I tablespoon balsamic vinegar
- I tablespoon runny honey

Red cabbage is so good for you, and so tangy and tasty. It also goes wonderfully with chicken or red meat dishes.

1. Heat the olive oil in a large non-stick pan, and sauté the onion for 3–4 minutes, until it starts to soften.

2. Add the cabbage, chopped apple, bay leaves, ground cinnamon and star anise and stir well.

3. Pour in the grape juice, balsamic vinegar and honey. Bring to the boil and cover, then reduce the heat and simmer over a low heat for 45–50 minutes, until the cabbage is soft. Remove the bay leaves and the star anise before serving.

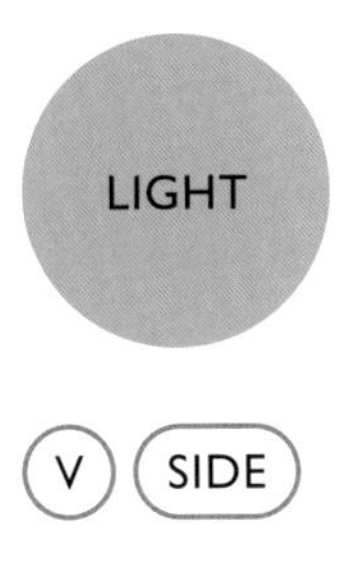

V SIDE

PUY LENTILS WITH SPINACH AND CAPERS

SERVES 4–6

1 tablespoon extra virgin olive oil
1 onion, peeled and finely chopped
1 garlic clove, peeled and crushed
250g Puy lentils, cooked (ready-cooked or cook your own according to the packet instructions)
300ml low-salt vegetable stock
50g capers
400g spinach leaves
a handful of finely chopped fresh flat-leaf parsley

A delicious and nutritious side dish that is high in fibre and packed with vitamins.

1. Heat the oil in a medium non-stick saucepan over a medium heat. Add the onion and garlic and sauté for 5 minutes until softened.

2. Add the lentils, stock and capers and simmer for a further 10 minutes.

3. Remove from the heat and stir through the spinach until it wilts, then finally add the parsley. Serve immediately.

Listen to your body. Sadly, it is impossible for me to be looking over your shoulder all the time – I can advise you, but I can't be there to make your decisions for you.

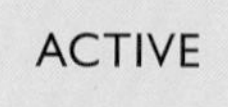

PEA & ASPARAGUS BRUSCHETTA

MAKES 12 BRUSCHETTA

1kg asparagus spears, trimmed and woody ends removed
150g frozen petit pois, thawed
a handful of fresh mint leaves, chopped
2–3 sprigs of lemon thyme, leaves removed and chopped
1 tablespoon extra virgin olive oil
150g cherry tomatoes, quartered
freshly ground black pepper, to taste
1 garlic clove, peeled and halved
12 slices of ciabatta bread
125g low-fat mozzarella cheese, diced

A twist on the Italian classic with green veggies that tick extra health boxes!

1. Blanch the trimmed asparagus spears with the peas in boiling water for about 3 minutes. Drain, refresh under cold water and set aside.

2. In a large bowl mix together the mint, lemon thyme, olive oil, cherry tomatoes and cooled asparagus and peas. Season with black pepper.

3. Preheat the grill, and while the grill is heating up, rub the two garlic halves over the bread slices and pop them on a baking tray. Pile the asparagus mixture onto the garlicky bread slices, sprinkle over the diced mozzarella and place under the grill for 2–3 minutes. Serve immediately.

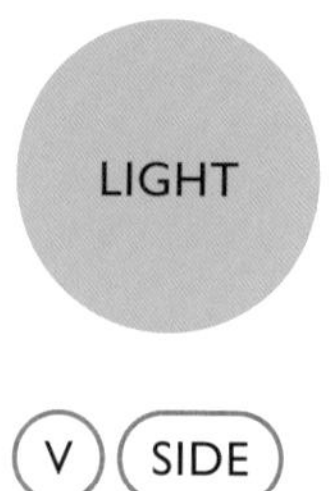

NUTMEG SPINACH

V SIDE

SERVES 4–6

I tablespoon extra virgin olive oil
I onion, peeled and finely chopped
I garlic clove, peeled and crushed
600g spinach leaves
freshly grated nutmeg, to taste
freshly ground black pepper, to taste

This is the most delicious way to serve spinach. You will love it!

1. Heat the oil in a large non-stick, lidded saucepan and sauté the onion and garlic for 3–4 minutes.

2. Add the spinach and cover with a lid until it has wilted. Season with plenty of nutmeg and black pepper and serve immediately.

There is no such thing as having a BAD DAY! You might have suffered a bad moment or made a bad choice, but that moment will pass and you can always rescue the rest of the day.

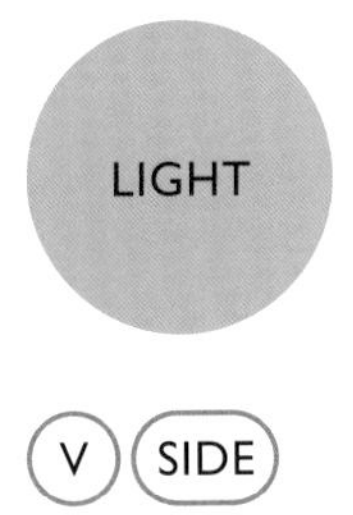

QUICK SPICED VEGGIES

V SIDE

SERVES 4–6

2 tablespoons extra virgin olive oil
1 onion, peeled and diced
1 garlic clove, peeled and crushed
½ teaspoon ground ginger
1 teaspoon garam masala
1 teaspoon chilli powder
1 teaspoon ground cumin
1 teaspoon ground coriander
2 cardamom pods, split open
3 tomatoes, diced
1 courgette, diced
2 red peppers, deseeded and sliced
1 head of broccoli, cut into florets
250g frozen peas, defrosted
freshly ground black pepper, to taste

Super fast, super spicy and super healthy!

1. Heat the olive oil in a large non-stick saucepan and sauté the onion and garlic for 2–3 minutes until softened. Stir in the ginger, garam masala, chilli powder, cumin, coriander and cardamom pods. Cook for 1 minute.

2. Add the tomatoes and 50ml warm water. Simmer, then add the courgette, peppers and broccoli. Cover and continue to cook for 5–6 minutes, or until the vegetables have softened.

3. Finally, stir in the peas and cook, uncovered, for a further 4–5 minutes until piping hot and the sauce has thickened. Remove the cardamom pods, season with black pepper and transfer to a serving bowl.

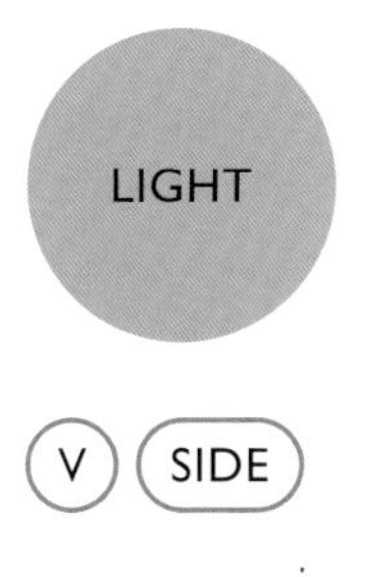

V SIDE

BEETROOT & SPINACH SUPERFOOD SALAD

SERVES 1 GENEROUSLY

- 100g baby spinach leaves
- 75g alfalfa sprouts
- 2 celery sticks, sliced
- 4 beetroot, cooked and peeled (see note), each cut into 8 wedges

FOR THE DRESSING:

- 4 tablespoons extra virgin olive oil
- 1½ tablespoons white wine vinegar
- 1 teaspoon wholegrain mustard
- 1 garlic clove, peeled and crushed
- 2 teaspoons runny honey
- 1 tablespoon snipped fresh chives
- 1 tablespoon chopped fresh parsley

This salad offers a powerful health boost that tastes great. Beetroot is jam-packed full of great vitamins and minerals, including iron, calcium, vitamin B6 and potassium. It helps to fight off infection and is also thought to protect against some cancers.

1. To make the dressing, whisk the oil, wine vinegar, wholegrain mustard, garlic, honey, chives and parsley together in a bowl until combined.

2. For the salad, put the spinach leaves, alfalfa sprouts and celery in another large bowl and mix together. Add the beetroot to the salad just before serving, so that it doesn't stain all the other ingredients. Mix well. Pour the dressing over the salad, toss and serve immediately.

NOTE: I like to buy fresh beetroot, then chop off the stalks and boil them for about 1 hour. Alternatively, you can buy ready-cooked, vacuum-packed beetroot from the supermarket.

BEETROOT SUPERFOOD SOUP

V

SERVES 4

- 1 tablespoon olive oil
- 1 small onion, peeled and finely chopped
- 400g raw beetroot, peeled and cut into 1cm cubes
- 200g potatoes, peeled and chopped into small cubes
- 1 litre hot, low-salt vegetable stock
- juice of 1 lemon
- freshly ground black pepper, to taste
- 2 tablespoons low-fat crème fraîche, to serve
- 2 tablespoons snipped chives, to serve

Beetroot is thought to be a true anti-cancer superfood, filled with anti-carcinogens. It tastes great too – especially in this really easy soup.

1. Heat the olive oil in a large saucepan over a medium heat, then add the onion and sauté for 5 minutes until it starts to soften.

2. Add the beetroot and potato and cook for a further 5 minutes, then add the stock and lemon juice, season with black pepper and bring to the boil. Reduce the heat and simmer gently, half covered, for about 25 minutes.

3. Allow to cool slightly, then blitz with a handheld stick blender or whiz in a liquidiser and reheat just before serving.

4. Serve with a swirl of low-fat crème fraîche and a sprinkling of chives.

No excuses! The fact is, being overweight causes health problems that can lead to an early death.

LIGHT

ACTIVE WITH BREAD

SUMMER CHICKPEA SOUP

V

SERVES 4–6

3 x 410g cans chickpeas, drained and rinsed
2 sprigs of rosemary
2 onions, peeled and finely chopped
4 garlic cloves, peeled and crushed
410g can chopped tomatoes
4 sun-dried tomatoes from a jar, drained on kitchen paper
1 low-salt vegetable stock cube
freshly ground black pepper, to taste
20g Parmesan or mature Cheddar cheese, grated
a small handful of fresh parsley, finely chopped
a few drops of chilli oil
2 teaspoons extra virgin olive oil

Due to their high fibre content, chickpeas are excellent for your Bikini Promise. They have a lovely nutty taste and will keep you feeling fuller for longer, helping to control your appetite.

1. Place the chickpeas in a large saucepan with the rosemary, onions, garlic, tomatoes, sun-dried tomatoes, stock cube and enough cold water to cover. Bring to the boil, cover, and simmer gently for 10 minutes.

2. Once the onion is soft, remove the pan from the heat and carefully remove the rosemary sprigs. With a handheld stick blender, blitz the soup until it reaches your preferred consistency. Bring the soup back to a simmer and season with black pepper.

3. To serve, ladle the soup into bowls, then sprinkle each serving with a little Parmesan and parsley, and dot with chilli oil and olive oil.

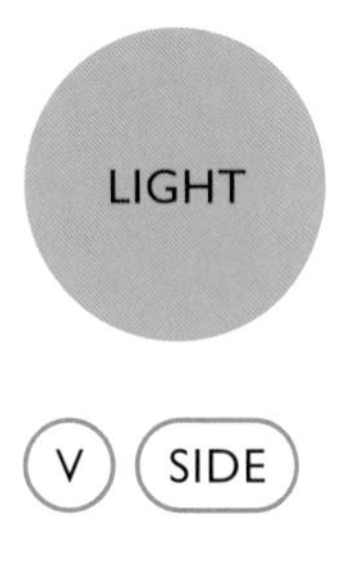

ULTIMATE TOMATO SUMMER SALAD

V SIDE

SERVES 4–6

A selection of ripe red, green and yellow tomatoes, all shapes and sizes

FOR THE DRESSING:
3 tablespoons extra virgin olive oil
3 tablespoons balsamic vinegar
2 teaspoons runny honey
2 teaspoons wholegrain mustard

I'm leaving the quantities of tomatoes for this dish up to you. It is basically a big plate piled high with colourful, sweet tomatoes of all shapes and sizes, with a delicious tangy dressing. If you are feeding a houseful, make more; if it is just for you, make less!

The quantities for the dressing serve around eight, but it will keep for a week in the fridge in a sealed jar.

Tomatoes are my No. 1 superfood! They are so jam-packed with goodness, you cannot go wrong, however you choose to eat them. Whether they're canned, cooked, raw or puréed, tomatoes always support a healthy eating plan.

1. Wash and slice all the tomatoes and set aside.

2. Whisk all the dressing ingredients together in a bowl, then pour the dressing over the tomatoes and let the dish sit at room temperature for a couple of hours before eating. The sweetness of the tomatoes is more pronounced when they are slightly warm.

TIP: Keep your tomatoes on a warm windowsill instead of in the fridge, so that their delicious sweetness develops naturally.

QUICK SPICY CHICKEN & LIME SALAD

SERVES 4

4 skinless chicken breasts
1 standard bag of mixed salad leaves
1 large carrot, grated
1 ripe avocado, halved, pitted, peeled and sliced
a handful of cherry tomatoes
4 spring onions, finely chopped
juice of 2 limes, to serve

FOR THE SPICE MIX:
½ teaspoon cayenne pepper
½ teaspoon mild chilli powder
1 teaspoon garlic granules (or 2 large cloves of garlic, crushed)
1 teaspoon dried basil
2 teaspoons brown sugar
zest of 1 lime
1 tablespoon extra virgin olive oil

This is a fantastically quick and easy meal. Although you need around 30 minutes to cook it, and 30 minutes marinating time, the prep can be done in less than 10 minutes, so you can get your nails painted while it's doing its thing!

1. Preheat the oven to 180°C/gas mark 4 and line a baking tray with foil.

2. Mix all the spice mix ingredients together, along with the lime zest and olive oil, and spread on both sides of the chicken breasts. Lay the breasts on the prepared baking tray, then leave to marinate for 30 minutes in the fridge.

3. Remove from the fridge and cook in the oven for about 25 minutes, then turn and cook for a further 5–10 minutes, depending on the size of the breasts, until cooked through.

4. Serve the cooked chicken on a bed of salad leaves with the grated carrot, avocado, tomatoes and spring onions, then drizzle the lime juice over the chicken and salad before serving.

ONE POT WONDERS

SALLY'S DO-IT-ALL TOMATO SAUCE

V

SERVES 4–6

- 1 large onion, peeled
- 2 garlic cloves, peeled
- ½ red chilli, deseeded and finely chopped (optional)
- 1 large carrot, peeled and roughly chopped
- 1 leek, washed, trimmed and roughly chopped
- 1 courgette, roughly chopped
- 1 red pepper, deseeded and roughly chopped
- 1 green pepper, deseeded and roughly chopped
- 1 yellow pepper, deseeded and roughly chopped
- 4 tablespoons extra virgin olive oil
- 2 x 400g cans chopped tomatoes
- 4 tablespoons tomato purée
- pinch of sea salt flakes
- freshly ground black pepper, to taste
- 1 teaspoon caster sugar
- 2 slurps Worcestershire sauce
- 2 slurps balsamic vinegar
- a handful of fresh basil leaves, chopped
- a handful of fresh parsley, chopped

Make a batch of this magical sauce once a week and keep it in the fridge or store in separate freezer bags and freeze until needed. It is jam-packed with antioxidants and is the perfect go-to sauce when running short on time while on your Bikini Promise.

You can heat separate portions and use it as a pasta sauce, a meatball sauce, as a casserole base, or serve it with chicken or fish. It can also be spiced up with extra chillies, or made into BBQ sauce by adding some smoked paprika.

1. Place the onion, garlic and red chilli in the bowl of a food-processor; blitz until finely chopped and then transfer the mixture to a bowl.

2. Place all the other vegetables in the food-processor and blitz until very finely chopped.

3. Heat 2 tablespoons of the olive oil in a large non-stick, lidded saucepan, and sauté the onion, garlic and chilli mixture for 7–10 minutes, stirring, until the onions start to soften and brown.

4. Add the chopped vegetables, along with the remaining olive oil. Cook over a medium heat, stirring regularly, for 20 minutes.

5. Add the chopped tomatoes, tomato purée, sugar, Worcestershire sauce and balsamic vinegar and season with salt and pepper. Stir well, cover, and simmer over a low heat for a further 30 minutes.

6. Finally, add the herbs and whiz with a handheld stick blender until the sauce has reached your desired consistency.

'I love cooking in this way, it's so simple and quick. The kids can have a big portion of rice with their meal to fill them up, and I can miss the carbs out, or just have a couple of spoonfuls of rice, with extra salad on the side. It's the perfect way to keep losing the pounds on the Bikini Promise.' SALLY

ACTIVE

VEGETARIAN CHILLI 3-IN-1

V

SERVES 4

- 1 tablespoon extra virgin olive oil
- 1 large onion, peeled and finely chopped
- 2 garlic cloves, peeled and crushed
- 2 red peppers, deseeded and sliced (or the equivalent in frozen pepper slices)
- 2 x 400g cans mixed beans, drained and rinsed
- 1 red chilli, deseeded and chopped, or 1 teaspoon chilli flakes
- 500g tomato passata
- 2 teaspoons light muscovado sugar
- 2 tablespoons balsamic vinegar

TO MAKE THE VEGETARIAN CHILLI FILO PIE:

- 1 packet (approx. 250g) filo pastry sheets
- olive oil, for drizzling

Beans and pulses contain as much protein as fillet steak, but at a fraction of the cost, and they have many more health benefits. They are high in fibre, folate, potassium and zinc.

You can make three separate dishes with the chilli:

1. CHILLI BEANS ON TOAST
Serve the chilli on slices of toasted whole-nutty bread or on rye crispbreads.

2. VEGETARIAN CHILLI PASTA
Serve with an 75g portion of wholewheat pasta and some salad.

3. VEGETARIAN CHILLI FILO PIE
Cover the chilli with filo pastry (see below), which makes for a lovely, crunchy, low-fat pie topping.

1. Heat the olive oil in a large non-stick saucepan and sauté the onion, garlic and sliced peppers for 4–5 minutes until they start to soften.

2. Add all the remaining ingredients and mix together thoroughly. Bring to the boil, then reduce the heat and simmer uncovered for 20 minutes.

3. At this stage you can serve the chilli as Chilli Beans on Toast or Vegetarian Chilli Pasta (remember to hover your hand over your plate for portion size – see page 16).

4. To make the Vegetarian Chilli Filo Pie, spoon the cooked chilli into a large pie dish or individual small ovenproof ramekins.

5. Take one sheet of filo pastry at a time and scrunch it up into a ball. Pop the balls on top of your pie(s), sprinkle with a tiny drizzle of olive oil and bake in a hot oven for 10 minutes, until the pastry has browned and the filling is piping hot (it doesn't take long to cook because the filo pastry is so light and thin).

ACTIVE

CHICKEN & MUSHROOM 3-IN-1 DISH 1: CASSEROLE

SERVES 4

6 tablespoons plain flour
freshly ground black pepper, to taste
1 tablespoon dried mixed herbs (I prefer the Italian mix)
1.5kg boneless, skinless chicken breast pieces, cut into strips
6 tablespoons extra virgin olive oil
2 large onions, peeled and chopped
900ml low-salt chicken or vegetable stock
900ml white wine (or grape or apple juice if you prefer)
2 large leeks, washed, trimmed and finely chopped
4 celery sticks, finely chopped
6 garlic cloves, peeled and crushed
freshly 450g button mushrooms, sliced
3 small cooked new potatoes per person, to serve
cooked fresh or frozen veggies, to serve

This 3-in-1 recipe is easy-peasy, and saves you so much time on busy nights – you can just pull a dish out of the freezer. However did people manage before the invention of freezers and microwaves?

1. Preheat the oven to 180°C/gas mark 4.

2. Mix the flour with a grind of black pepper and the dried herbs in a large bowl. Roll the chicken strips in the flour mixture until well coated, reserving the remaining flour to thicken the sauce.

3. Heat the olive oil in a large, lidded flameproof casserole over a medium heat. Add the floured chicken strips and fry until they are pale gold all over. Add the onions and continue frying for a few minutes until they start to soften.

4. Add the stock, wine, leeks, celery, garlic and mushrooms. Mix the reserved flour with a little cold water to form a thin paste and add this to the casserole. Cover and cook in the oven for 20 minutes, until the chicken is tender.

5. Divide into three portions, and place two of the portions in foil freezer dishes. Leave to cool, then cover, label and pop in the freezer, to make the other two dishes.

6. Divide the remaining chicken casserole into four portions and serve with small new potatoes and plenty of fresh vegetables.

ACTIVE

DISH 2:

CHICKEN & SWEETCORN PIE

SERVES 4

I portion of Chicken and Mushroom Casserole, defrosted (see page 62)
I cup frozen sweetcorn
½ cup frozen peas
8 sheets filo pastry
a little olive oil, for brushing
mixed green salad, to serve

1. Preheat the oven to 200°C/gas mark 6.

2. Place the defrosted Chicken and Mushroom Casserole in a large, deep pie dish and add the peas and sweetcorn. Mix well to combine.

3. Scrunch the sheets of filo pastry into loose balls and place them on top of the casserole, spreading the folds so that you completely cover the top of the pie. Brush with olive oil and bake for 10–25 minutes, until the top is crisp and browned and the filling is piping hot. Serve immediately, with a fresh mixed green salad.

TIP: Thinking and planning ahead makes life so much easier when you have made the Bikini Promise. Defrost your frozen portions overnight in the fridge, and make sure you've got all the other ingredients you need. You can then quickly put it together for lunch or dinner without being tempted to dive into the biscuit box because you haven't got anything healthy and ready to eat.

Make changes NOW so that you can enjoy a full and healthy life.

ACTIVE

DISH 3:

THAI GREEN CURRY

SERVES 4

300g brown basmati rice (75g per person)
1 tablespoon extra virgin olive oil
1 green pepper, deseeded and sliced
1 red pepper, deseeded and sliced
a handful of mangetout or sugarsnap peas
2 tablespoons Thai green curry paste
1 small red chilli, deseeded and finely chopped
a handful of baby sweetcorn
1 portion of Chicken and Mushroom Casserole, defrosted (see page 62)
a handful of fresh coriander, chopped, to serve
a handful of cashew nuts, chopped, to serve

1. Cook the rice according to the packet instructions (no need to add salt).

2. Meanwhile, heat the olive oil in a large frying pan, then add the red and green peppers and the mangetout or sugarsnap peas and fry for a few minutes, until softened. Add the green curry paste, the chilli, the baby sweetcorn and a tablespoon of water, stir well for a few minutes, then add the defrosted chicken casserole to the pan. Cook for a further 7–8 minutes, until all the flavours have infused and the meat is piping hot.

3. Once the rice is cooked, drain and pop into bowls. Top each serving with the chicken curry and sprinkle coriander and cashew nuts on top.

TIP: If you are in a hurry, microwave rice portions are great. Just buy brown rice and watch your portion size!

ACTIVE

PORK 3-IN-1 DISH 1: CASSEROLE

SERVES 4

- 1 sweet potato per person, peeled and cut into wedges
- 4 tablespoons extra virgin olive oil
- 2 tablespoons plain flour
- freshly ground black pepper
- 2 teaspoons dried rosemary
- 1.5kg pork fillet or lean pork loin, fat removed, cut into 2cm cubes
- 1 red pepper, deseeded and thinly sliced
- 2 bunches spring onions, chopped
- 6 celery sticks, chopped
- 300g whole small chestnut or button mushrooms
- 4 garlic cloves, crushed
- 2cm piece of fresh root ginger, peeled and grated
- 2 x 400g cans chopped tomatoes
- 6 tablespoons tomato purée
- a handful of fresh basil, roughly chopped
- 2 teaspoons runny honey
- 2 teaspoons wholegrain mustard
- 450ml low-salt chicken stock
- 2 slurps Worcestershire sauce
- fresh or frozen vegetables of your choice, to serve

Here is another recipe that can be split and made into 3 dishes. This first dish is served with sweet potato wedges.

1. Preheat the oven to 200°C/gas mark 6.

2. Put the sweet potato wedges in a bowl with 2 tablespoons of olive oil and toss them with your hands until they are covered in the oil. Arrange them on a baking tray, then put to one side until the pork is ready to go in the oven.

3. Mix the flour, black pepper and rosemary together in a large bowl. Drop in the pork cubes and coat them in the seasoned flour mix.

4. Heat the remaining oil in a large, heavy-based non-stick frying pan over a high heat, then add the floured pork pieces and cook until the pork starts to brown (you may need to do this in batches if your pan isn't big enough). Remove the pork from the frying pan, place in a large, lidded flameproof casserole and set aside.

5. Add the red pepper, spring onions, celery and mushrooms to the frying pan, and cook for a few minutes, stirring frequently, to soften, then add the garlic, ginger, chopped tomatoes, tomato purée, basil, honey, mustard, stock and the Worcestershire sauce and bring to the boil. Reduce the heat and simmer for 10 minutes, uncovered, to allow some of the liquid to evaporate.

6. Pour the sauce over the pork in the casserole dish, cover with the lid and pop in the oven. Cook for 30 minutes, then place the sweet potato wedges in the oven on a lower shelf and continue cooking for a further hour, until the sweet potatoes are cooked and brown all over.

7. Check that the pork is cooked through and that the sauce has thickened, then remove the casserole and sweet potato wedges from the oven.

8. Divide into three portions, and place two of the portions in foil freezer dishes. Leave to cool, then cover, label and pop in the freezer, to make the other two dishes.

9. Divide the remaining casserole portion into four, and serve with the sweet potato wedges and lots of vegetables.

ACTIVE

DISH 2:

SWEET & SOUR PORK WITH PINEAPPLE

SERVES 4

- 300g brown basmati rice (75g per person)
- 2 tablespoons extra virgin olive oil
- 1 yellow pepper, deseeded and sliced
- 1 green pepper, deseeded and sliced
- 1 portion of Pork Casserole (see page 66), defrosted
- ½ medium pineapple, peeled, cored and cut into chunks
- 2 tablespoons white wine vinegar
- 1 tablespoon runny honey
- a handful of chopped coriander, to serve

1. Cook the rice according to the packet instructions (no need to add salt).

2. Meanwhile, heat the olive oil in a large, heavy-based non-stick frying pan, then add the sliced peppers and fry until they start to soften.

3. Add the defrosted Pork Casserole and heat through thoroughly, until the meat is piping hot, then add the pineapple chunks, white wine vinegar and honey, and simmer for a few more minutes.

4. Once the rice is cooked, drain and pop into bowls. Top each bowl with a portion of the sweet and sour pork, and sprinkle with chopped coriander. Serve immediately.

Meal matching is quite simply matching the food you eat to your activities.

ACTIVE

DISH 3:

PORK NOODLES & CASHEW NUTS

SERVES 4

4 portions egg noodles
2 tablespoons extra virgin olive oil
1 yellow pepper, deseeded and sliced
1 green pepper, deseeded and sliced
1 carrot, peeled, sliced and cut into matchsticks
1 portion Pork Casserole (see page 66), defrosted
125g fine green beans or mangetout, sliced
125g beansprouts
50g cashew nuts, roughly chopped
1 tablespoon soy sauce

1. Cook the noodles according to the packet instructions, then drain and set aside.

2. Heat the olive oil in a large, heavy-based non-stick frying pan, add the sliced peppers and carrot and fry for 2 minutes until softened.

3. Add the defrosted Pork Casserole and cook over a high heat for 5–6 minutes, stirring, until the meat is piping hot.

4. Add the green beans or mangetout and cook for a further 2–3 minutes, then stir in the beansprouts. Simmer for a few minutes, then add the chopped cashew nuts.

5. Finally, stir in the drained noodles and the soy sauce and check that it is thoroughly hot and bubbling before serving.

ACTIVE

SLOW COOKED PULLED BRISKET

SERVES 4

2 tablespoons extra virgin olive oil
1kg boned and rolled beef brisket trimmed of any excess fat
2 large onions, peeled and sliced
3 celery sticks, chopped
2 carrots, peeled and sliced
250g large flat mushrooms, stalks chopped and heads thinly sliced
550ml brown ale or stout
a few fresh sprigs of thyme
2 bay leaves
2 teaspoons light muscovado sugar
freshly ground black pepper, to taste
900g sweet potatoes, peeled and chopped
dash of milk
1 tablespoon Dijon mustard
a handful of chopped fresh parsley or thyme, to serve

Brisket is a relatively inexpensive cut of meat, but it does take long, slow cooking to make it really tender.

1. Preheat the oven to 190°C/gas mark 5.

2. Heat the olive oil in a deep, flameproof casserole and brown the brisket all over. Remove from the pan and set aside.

3. Reduce the heat and fry the onions, celery, carrots and mushrooms for 6–8 minutes, stirring regularly.

4. Return the beef to the casserole and add the ale or stout, thyme, bay leaves and muscovado sugar. Add water if necessary, so that the liquid comes about two-thirds up the beef. Season with black pepper, bring to a simmer, cover tightly, and transfer to the oven for 20 minutes.

5. After 20 minutes, reduce the heat to 160°C/gas mark 3 and cook for 3 hours, turning the meat twice, until it is tender.

6. Meanwhile, in a large heavy pan, boil the chopped sweet potatoes for 20–25 minutes. Drain and mash, adding a dash of milk to reach the right consistency.

7. Once the beef is tender, remove the casserole from the oven and wrap the beef in foil. Set aside to rest.

8. Use a slotted spoon to remove the vegetables and herbs from the casserole dish and set them aside in a warm bowl.

9. Pop the casserole back on the hob, increase the heat and let the sauce bubble away and reduce for 5–6 minutes, then whisk in the mustard and pour the sauce into a jug.

10. Prepare the brisket for serving by pulling apart the meat using two forks.

11. Serve the pulled brisket on a bed of sweet potato mash, loaded up with the veggies. Sprinkle with the parsley or thyme and serve with extra fresh veggies of your choice, and the sauce on the side.

SUMMER SLIM BEEF 2-IN-1 DISH 1: CASSOULET

SERVES 4

2 tablespoons plain flour
freshly ground black pepper
1 teaspoon dried oregano
1kg lean beef stewing steak, cut into 1cm cubes
2 tablespoons olive oil
freshly 2 large onions, peeled and finely chopped
1 green pepper, deseeded and finely chopped
4 garlic cloves, peeled and crushed
1 leek, washed, trimmed and thinly sliced
2 celery sticks, finely chopped
2 x 400g cans chopped tomatoes
4 tablespoons tomato purée
1 tablespoon paprika
a pinch of freshly grated nutmeg, or ground nutmeg
300ml low-salt beef stock
1 teaspoon caster sugar

TO SERVE
300g brown rice (75g per person)
dollop of low-fat crème fraîche
2 spring onions, finely chopped

Both this Beef Cassoulet and the Chilli con Carne overleaf are seriously easy to make and are perfect tummy fillers, packed with goodness but low in fat. You can serve them without the rice if you prefer, for a low-carb, low-fat meal that looks, smells and tastes absolutely delicious!

Serve either dish with a huge mixed salad with lots of colour: green leaves, red tomatoes, black grapes, yellow peppers and a sprinkling of sunflower seeds or pumpkin seeds.

You will need two separate lidded casserole dishes.

1. Preheat the oven to 180°C/gas mark 4.

2. Mix the flour with the black pepper and dried oregano in a large bowl. Add the cubed beef and coat it with the seasoned flour. Set aside.

3. Heat the olive oil in a large non-stick frying pan, add the onions and pepper and cook gently, stirring frequently, for 3–4 minutes.

4. Increase the heat, add the floured meat and fry on all sides until the meat is browned.

5. Add the garlic, leek, celery, chopped tomatoes, tomato purée, paprika, nutmeg, beef stock and sugar, cook for a few minutes and then divide between two separate casserole dishes.

6. Cover both casserole dishes and cook in the oven for 1½–2 hours, until the meat is lovely and tender. Place half the cassoulet in a foil freezer dish. Leave to cool, then cover, label and pop in the freezer.

7. Cook the rice according to the packet instructions and divide between four plates. Top with a portion of Summer Slim Beef Cassoulet and a swirl of crème fraîche mixed with the spring onions.

DISH 2:

CHILLI CON CARNE

SERVES 4

I portion of Beef Cassoulet (see page 71), defrosted
400g can red kidney beans, drained
I small red chilli, deseeded and finely chopped
8 soft wholemeal flour tortillas, warmed
a handful mature Cheddar cheese, grated
green salad, to serve

I. Add the drained kidney beans and the chopped red chilli to the cassoulet and reheat until piping hot.

2. Divide between four bowls and top each serving with a sprinkle of grated cheese. Serve with warmed tortillas and a green salad to complete the meal.

Your body needs a 12-hour break without food, so always have your last meal of the day 12 hours before you are due to have your breakfast.

LIGHT WHEN SERVED WITH RICE

SWEET PEPPER RAGU

V

SERVES 4–6

- 3 tablespoons olive oil
- 2 garlic cloves, peeled and crushed
- 2 red onions, peeled and sliced
- 3 red peppers, deseeded and sliced
- 3 orange peppers, deseeded and sliced
- 2 green peppers, deseeded and sliced
- 2 sticks of celery, sliced
- 400g can chopped tomatoes
- a slurp Worcestershire sauce
- freshly ground black pepper, to taste
- 2 tablespoons dried Italian mixed herbs
- 18 black olives, pitted and halved
- a handful of fresh basil, chopped

This is seriously easy to make – it just takes a bit of patience, as you wait for it to cook down and release all of its gorgeous sweet pepper flavours. This is one of those dishes that tastes even better the next day (and the day after that!).

Serve it on its own as a soup or stew, or as a sauce for pasta or rice. It's also delicious with fish and chicken; the choice is yours.

1. Heat the olive oil in a large non-stick pan over a medium heat, then add the garlic, onion, peppers and celery and fry, stirring frequently for 3–4 minutes until everything is soft. Reduce the heat, cover, and let it cook, very gently, for around 30 minutes. Every once in a while, take the lid off and give it a stir.

2. After the peppers have been cooking for 30 minutes, add the chopped tomatoes, Worcestershire sauce, black pepper and mixed herbs.

3. Continue to cook for a further 30 minutes, then add the olives and chopped basil 5 minutes before serving.

ACTIVE

V

PEA RISOTTO WITH BUTTERNUT SQUASH

SERVES 4

500g butternut squash, peeled, deseeded and cut into 2cm chunks
2 tablespoons extra virgin olive oil
1 onion, peeled and finely chopped
1 garlic clove, peeled and crushed
250g Arborio rice
1 teaspoon fennel seeds, crushed
pinch of cayenne pepper
200ml white wine
900ml low-salt vegetable stock
325g frozen peas, defrosted
grated zest and juice of 1 unwaxed lemon
a handful of fresh mint leaves, chopped, to garnish
lemon wedges, to serve

Risotto is traditionally made using butter, cream and cheese, but this fresh and summery alternative is a light, low-fat version. Just remember to hover your hand over your plate to get the right portion size for you.

1. Preheat the oven to 200°C/gas mark 6 and line a large baking tray with baking parchment.

2. Spread the chunks of butternut squash on the prepared baking tray in a single layer, and drizzle with 1 tablespoon of the olive oil. Bake in the oven for about 30 minutes, until soft and slightly browned.

3. Heat the remaining olive oil in a large, non-stick lidded frying pan over a high heat, add the onion and garlic and fry gently for a few minutes until the onion is soft.

4. Add the rice, fennel seeds, cayenne pepper and white wine, and stir constantly over a medium heat until the wine has been absorbed.

5. Start adding the vegetable stock slowly, a ladle at a time. As you are stirring the rice, you will see when each addition of liquid has been absorbed. This shows it's time to add another ladleful.

6. After about 20 minutes, when the rice is cooked, add the defrosted peas, the lemon zest and the lemon juice, and heat through.

7. Finally, add the roasted butternut squash and a sprinkle of fresh mint, and serve immediately with a lemon wedge on the side.

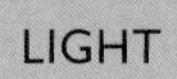

FENNEL & SEAFOOD ONE-POT

SERVES 4

2 tablespoons extra virgin olive oil
1 medium carrot, peeled, washed and finely chopped
1 celery stick, finely chopped
1 fennel bulb, cored and sliced thinly, green leafy fronds reserved for garnishing (if your fennel has them intact)
1 medium onion, peeled and chopped
1 garlic clove, peeled and crushed
1 teaspoon fennel seeds
125ml orange juice
410g can chopped tomatoes
250ml fish stock (or vegetable stock)
200g bag frozen mixed seafood or frozen fish pie mix, defrosted

This dish could not be easier, tastier or healthier. So simple, yet filled with delicious, fresh flavours. I use a frozen seafood mix, but you could use frozen fish pie mix if you prefer.

1. Heat the olive oil in a heavy-based saucepan over a medium heat, then add the chopped vegetables, onion, garlic and fennel seeds and sauté for 3–4 minutes, until the onion turns translucent.

2. Add the orange juice, chopped tomatoes and stock. Bring to the boil, then reduce the heat and simmer gently for 15 minutes.

3. Pop the defrosted seafood into the pan and stir well. Bring back to the boil and simmer for 6–8 minutes, ensuring the seafood is thoroughly cooked.

4. Ladle into bowls and garnish with chopped fennel fronds, if you have them. Serve immediately.

ACTIVE

ONE POT CHICKEN 'N' RICE

SERVES 2

- 2 tablespoons extra virgin olive oil
- 1 onion, peeled and chopped
- 1 garlic clove, peeled and crushed
- 2 teaspoons medium curry paste
- 2 skinless chicken breast fillets, cut into thin strips
- 80g basmati rice
- 280ml low-salt chicken stock
- 200g frozen mixed vegetables
- 200g frozen spinach

This is a dish that I've taught my children to cook. It couldn't be easier and I hope it proves that eating fresh and healthy ingredients doesn't have to cost a fortune or take hours to cook. Everyone is capable of dishes like these!

1. Heat the olive oil in a large non-stick saucepan, and add the onion, garlic and curry paste. Cook for 2–3 minutes, stirring frequently, until the onion softens. Add the chicken breast strips and fry for a further 2–3 minutes until browned.

2. Stir in the rice and cook for 1 minute, then pour in the chicken stock. Stir, bring to the boil, then reduce the heat, cover and simmer for about 10 minutes, stirring regularly, until the stock is absorbed and the rice is tender.

3. Stir in all the frozen vegetables and spinach and cook, uncovered, for 5 minutes until heated through, then serve immediately.

If you haven't eaten for 3 or 4 hours and feel hungry, you know this is a 'need' meal, which should be nutritious.

LIGHT

V

CAULIFLOWER & CHICKPEA TAGINE

SERVES 2

2 tablespoons extra virgin olive oil
1 large onion, sliced
1 garlic clove, crushed
2 teaspoons ground cinnamon
2 teaspoons ground cumin
2 teaspoons ground coriander
2cm piece fresh ginger, grated
1 cauliflower, cut into florets
½ butternut squash, peeled, deseeded and cut into 4cm pieces
1 large aubergine, cut into 4cm pieces
500ml low salt vegetable stock
400g can chopped tomatoes
2 teaspoons harissa paste
400g can chickpeas, drained
zest from 1 lemon
freshly ground black pepper
handful fresh parsley, chopped
handful fresh coriander, chopped

This is the tastiest vegetable tagine you will ever eat. If you eat meat, having two meat free days a week is of great benefit. Not only does it focus your mind on upping your vegetable intake, it gives your system a rest from meat and offers a better, healthier balance.

1. Heat the olive oil in a large, lidded non-stick pan and add the onion. Cook for 4–5 minutes until translucent.

2. Next stir in the garlic, ground spices and ginger, then fry for a further 2 minutes.

3. Now stir in the cauliflower, butternut squash and aubergine. Add vegetable stock, tomatoes and harissa paste. Simmer for 15 minutes, or until the vegetables are tender.

4. Finally, add the chickpeas, lemon zest and freshly ground black pepper. Simmer, covered, for a further 5 minutes. Sprinkle with the chopped herbs and serve.

ACTIVE

BEEF ROULADES WITH HEALTHY COLESLAW

SERVES 4

1 tablespoon plain flour
freshly ground black pepper
1 teaspoon garlic granules
4 slices of beef rump steak, fat trimmed off
4 teaspoons horseradish
coarse sea salt flakes
2 carrots, peeled and cut into thin strips, lengthwise
1 onion, peeled and finely chopped
1 celery stick, cut into thin strips lengthwise
2 tablespoons extra virgin olive oil
450ml tomato juice
5 tablespoons red wine
1 teaspoon wholegrain mustard
1 generous slurp of Worcestershire sauce
1 tablespoon redcurrant jelly

FOR THE COLESLAW:
6 tablespoons fat-free crème fraîche
½ teaspoon Dijon mustard
2 tablespoons mayonnaise
½ white cabbage, tough core removed and shredded
2 carrots, peeled and grated
½ onion, peeled and sliced

I often get asked about the health benefits of eating red meat, and if it is OK as part of a healthy eating plan. My advice, if you are a meat eater, is to have red meat a maximum of three times a week. Ensure it is always lean, cut off any visible fat and enjoy the fact that it is high in protein and iron.

Although all of my Bikini Promise recipes are suitable as 'everyday' recipes, this is one that looks impressive (and tastes amazing!) and is posh enough to be served at a dinner party. You can serve it with delicious new potatoes, but on the Bikini Promise, serve it without carbs.

1. Preheat the oven to 150°C/gas mark 2.

2. Mix the flour with the black pepper and garlic granules in a bowl, then set aside.

3. Place the slices of beef between two sheets of clingfilm and beat with a rolling pin until they are very thin. Remove the clingfilm. Spread each slice with a spoonful of horseradish and season with black pepper and a tiny pinch of sea salt flakes.

4. Lay the sliced carrots, onion and celery on top and roll up each slice into a tight roll. Fasten with string or a toothpick, then roll the roulades in the flour mixture to coat.

5. Heat the olive oil in a large non-stick frying pan and brown the roulades on all sides.

6. Add the tomato juice, wine, mustard, Worcestershire sauce and redcurrant jelly and bring to the boil, then transfer to a casserole, cover with foil and bake for about 2 hours, until the meat is tender and the sauce has reduced. If necessary, take the foil off for the last 10 minutes, to help the sauce reduce.

7. To make the healthy coleslaw, mix together the fat-free crème fraîche, Dijon mustard, mayonnaise (not low fat – it's not pleasant. It's much better to have the real thing, but less of it!), shredded white cabbage, grated carrot and sliced onion.

TEN MINUTES FROM START TO FINISH

ACTIVE

RAINBOW PASTA LUNCHBOX

(V)

SERVES 1

75g penne pasta (or your favourite shape)
1 teaspoon olive oil
1 tablespoon sun-dried tomato pesto
freshly ground black pepper, to taste
85g baby plum tomatoes, halved
50g light mozzarella, cubed
3–4 pitted black olives, thinly sliced
a handful of basil leaves

Scientific research has demonstrated that carbohydrates such as pasta are higher in calories when cooked and eaten hot straight away, than when they're left to go cold. It sounds too good to be true, but cooled pasta becomes more fibrous, and even more carbohydrate is broken down into fibre if the cold pasta is then reheated. So, you can happily take your pasta dinner to work the next day, pop it in the microwave, and it will be even better for you. Honestly!

1. Cook the pasta according to the packet instructions. Drain, rinse under cold water to cool, then drain thoroughly. Toss with the oil and sun-dried tomato pesto, then season with freshly ground black pepper.

2. Place the pasta in a jar or plastic box and scatter over the remaining ingredients in layers, finishing with the basil. Seal with a lid and keep in the fridge, for eating hot or cold, for lunch the next day.

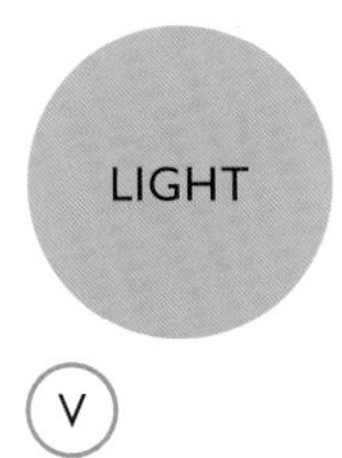

PESTO TOMATOES ON TOAST

SERVES 2

2 slices of whole-nutty bread
small amount of butter
4 large 'on the vine' tomatoes, sliced
2 teaspoons red pesto
olive oil, for drizzling
freshly ground black pepper, to taste

This must be one of the most nutritious breakfasts on record. The recipe serves two people, but you can just as easily make it for less or more.

1. Preheat the grill to high.

2. Grill the bread lightly on both sides and butter.

3. Place the tomato slices on the toasted bread.

4. Drop a little dollop of red pesto on top of each tomato and drizzle a tiny bit of olive oil on top. Sprinkle with freshly ground black pepper.

5. Grill for 3–4 minutes, or until the tomatoes and pesto are warmed through and bubbling a bit.

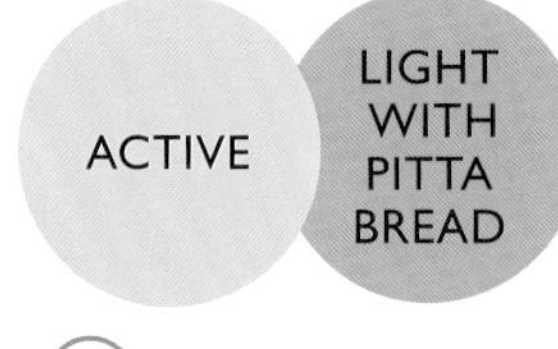

HEALTHY HOME-MADE HUMMUS

SERVES 2

2 small garlic cloves, peeled and roughly chopped
1 mild red chilli, deseeded and roughly chopped
400g can chickpeas, drained and rinsed
4 tablespoons extra virgin olive oil
a handful of fresh parsley or coriander leaves, chopped
juice of ½ lemon
pinch of sea salt and freshly ground black pepper

Serve with fresh vegetable crudités or with a toasted wholemeal pitta bread as an ACTIVE meal portion.

1. Put the garlic and chilli in a food-processor and blitz until finely chopped.

2. Add the drained chickpeas and two tablespoons of the olive oil and blitz until completely smooth – this may take several minutes. Add the herbs and a dash of lemon juice and blitz again until well blended. Taste, add more lemon juice and olive oil, as needed, and season with salt and pepper.

3. Spoon into a serving bowl, drizzle over a little dash of olive oil, then cover and chill until ready to serve.

CREAMY SALMON PARCELS

SERVES 2

- 4 heaped tablespoons low-fat crème fraîche, plus 2 tablespoons to serve
- 1 tablespoon chopped fresh tarragon
- freshly ground black pepper, to taste
- 2 skinless salmon fillets
- 1 large leek, washed, trimmed and thinly sliced
- 70g French green beans, trimmed
- 50g frozen peas

Using the microwave for this dish makes it super quick, and retains all the goodness in the veggies. If you don't have a microwave you can wrap the salmon in foil instead of greaseproof paper, and bake in the oven for 20 minutes at 180°C/gas mark 4 (do not use foil in the microwave).

1. Cut out two large squares of greaseproof paper measuring roughly 40cm across. Place the paper squares on a microwavable plate.

2. Mix the crème fraîche with the chopped tarragon and a sprinkle of black pepper in a bowl and set aside.

3. Pop a fillet of salmon in the centre of each piece of paper and top with the leek, French beans and peas. Dollop 2 tablespoons of the crème fraîche mixture on top.

4. Pull up the sides of the paper to make a parcel, twisting it at the top. Ensure you leave enough space inside the parcel for air to circulate.

5. Microwave on full power for 5 minutes, then leave to stand for 5 minutes, before serving with an extra dollop of crème fraîche.

ACTIVE

(V)

ORZO PASTA WITH SUNBLUSH TOMATOES

SERVES 4

approx. 20 cherry tomatoes, halved
2 sweet red Romano peppers, deseeded and cut into chunks (or regular red peppers)
8 shallots, peeled and halved
1 whole garlic bulb, unpeeled, with the top sliced off
extra virgin olive oil, for drizzling
2–3 sprigs fresh rosemary (or 2 teaspoons dried rosemary)
1 teaspoon dried oregano
1 teaspoon celery salt
1 teaspoon garlic granules
240g orzo pasta
freshly ground black pepper, to taste

I've added this dish into the 10-minute chapter as I like to cook the sunblush tomatoes ahead of time, even sometimes a day before, then add them to the orzo pasta after they've been sitting at room temperature for an hour or so. This enables you to make a fast dish that is already part prepared.

1. Preheat the oven to 200°C/gas mark 6.

2. Place all the vegetables and the garlic on a large baking tray and drizzle them with a little olive oil.

3. Sprinkle over the herbs, celery salt and garlic granules.

4. Bake in the oven for about 50 minutes, turning the peppers halfway through cooking.

5. Meanwhile, cook the orzo pasta according to the packet instructions, timing it so that everything will finish cooking at the same time.

6. Drain the pasta and serve it topped with the roasted tomatoes, peppers and onions and season with black pepper.

7. Finally, squeeze out the sweet, soft garlic flesh from the husk, and place a little on top of each portion.

LIGHT

HEALTHY STEAK & MUSHROOM STROGANOFF

SERVES 2

I tablespoon extra virgin olive oil
I large onion, peeled and finely chopped
2 garlic cloves, peeled and crushed
I teaspoon paprika
I green pepper, deseeded and sliced
200g button mushrooms
2 tablespoons red wine vinegar
150ml low-salt beef stock
2 teaspoons capers (optional)
200g lean rump steak, cut into thick slices and fat removed
150g low-fat fromage frais
freshly ground black pepper, to taste
cooked brown rice, to serve

You can easily make this a vegetarian dish by leaving out the steak and doubling up on the mushrooms!

1. Heat the olive oil in a large non-stick frying pan, add the onion and sauté for a few minutes until soft.

2. Add the garlic and paprika and cook for 1–2 minutes, then add the sliced pepper and mushrooms (double quantities of mushrooms if you're leaving out the meat) and continue cooking for a further 5–8 minutes until softened.

3. Add the red wine vinegar, stock and the capers, if using. Bring to the boil, then reduce the heat and simmer gently for 4–5 minutes, until the sauce thickens slightly.

4. Finally, add the sliced beef and cook for 2–3 minutes, depending on how rare you like it, then stir in the fromage frais and season with plenty of black pepper. Divide between two bowls and serve with brown rice.

Hover your hand!
It's all about portion size, and YOUR hand relates perfectly to YOUR portion size.

LIGHT

ACTIVE WITH RICE

STIR-FRIED BEEF & CASHEW NUTS

SERVES 4

2 teaspoons sesame oil
1 tablespoon soy sauce
1 tablespoon runny honey
2cm piece of fresh root ginger, peeled and grated
2 garlic cloves, peeled and crushed
300g beef rump steak cut into thin strips, all visibile fat removed
1 tablespoon olive oil
1 onion, peeled and sliced
a handful of cashew nuts
chopped fresh coriander, to serve

I ask my friendly local butcher to cut the meat for me so that it's extra thin. Make sure you don't use salted or roasted cashew nuts... they are not part of the Bikini Promise!

1. Whisk together the sesame oil, soy sauce, honey, ginger and garlic in a non-metallic bowl. Add the beef strips and leave to marinate in the fridge for 1–2 hours, then drain the strips, reserving the marinade.

2. Heat the olive oil in a large frying pan or wok and fry the onion for 2 minutes, then add the beef strips and stir-fry for 1 minute.

3. Add the reserved marinade and stir-fry for another minute, then stir in the cashew nuts to heat through.

4. Serve with steamed mangetout and baby sweetcorn, or basmati rice, and sprinkle with coriander before serving.

ACTIVE

CAJUN CHICKEN SALAD OPEN SANDWICH

SERVES 4

2 skinless chicken breasts, sliced into thin strips
1 tablespoon Cajun spice mix
extra virgin olive oil, for drizzling
4 slices of brown whole-nutty bread, lightly buttered
lemon wedges, to serve

FOR THE SALAD SANDWICHES:
1 standard bag of watercress (I like the bags with beetroot strips in, for added goodness)
1 red pepper, deseeded and sliced
1 ripe avocado, halved, pitted, peeled and sliced
sweet chilli sauce, to serve

A simple chicken sandwich that tastes this good – how is it possible?

1. Dust the chicken breasts with the Cajun spice mix.

2. Heat a little olive oil into a large non-stick frying pan and cook the chicken over a medium heat for 5–6 minutes, until it is cooked all the way through. Remove from the heat and set aside for a few minutes to rest while you arrange the sandwiches.

3. Put a bunch of watercress onto each slice of buttered bread. Arrange the sliced pepper and avocado on top and finish off with the cooked chicken strips.

4. Serve as open sandwiches, with lemon wedges on the side and a drizzle of sweet chilli sauce.

Today is another chance to get even healthier – and slimmer!

CHUPPA CO
STAINLESS STEEL

TWENTY MINUTES FROM START TO FINISH

ACTIVE

TURKEY BURGER ON A SWEET POTATO FRITTER

SERVES 4

FOR THE TURKEY BURGERS:

500g very lean turkey mince
2 garlic cloves, peeled and crushed
1 shallot, peeled and finely diced
2 teaspoons ground cumin
1 teaspoon dried oregano
½ red chilli, deseeded and very finely chopped
1 free-range egg
freshly ground black pepper, to taste
extra virgin olive oil, for frying

FOR THE SWEET POTATO FRITTERS:

800g sweet potatoes, peeled and cut into chunks
a handful of fresh parsley, chopped
a handful of fresh coriander, chopped
1 free-range egg, lightly beaten
1 tablespoon plain flour
green salad, to serve

This is great for every day eating – but even better when shared with friends. Even party food can be good for you!

1. Place the sweet potato chunks in boiling water and cook until just tender, then drain and roughly mash. Allow to cool.

2. Put the turkey mince, garlic, shallot, cumin, oregano, chilli and egg in a large bowl and mix well to combine. Season with ground black pepper. Divide the mince mixture into four, and shape each piece into a burger. Set aside.

3. In a separate bowl, mix the parsley and coriander with the beaten egg and flour and add to the cooled sweet potato. Shape into four large, flat fritters.

4. Heat a little olive oil in a large non-stick frying pan and cook the fritters over a medium heat for 4–5 minutes on each side.

5. Meanwhile, add a teaspoon of olive oil to a separate large non-stick frying pan, and cook the turkey burgers for 10–15 minutes, turning once, until cooked through. Serve each burger on a sweet potato fritter bed, with a big green side salad.

LIGHT

LOW-FAT TOMATO FILO TART

(V)

SERVES 4

4 sheets of filo pastry
2 tablespoons olive oil
½ teaspoon ground coriander
½ teaspoon fennel seeds
3 spring onions, sliced
1 teaspoon cumin seeds
2 garlic cloves, peeled and sliced
¼ teaspoon chilli powder
6 large, ripe tomatoes, each cut into 4 thick slices

This recipe has quite a few spices included. They are not expensive to buy and will be used again and again, so it's worth updating your spice rack with a fresh batch now you are on the Bikini Promise.

1. Preheat the oven to 220°C/gas mark 7, and place a non-stick baking tray in the oven.

2. Lightly brush each filo sheet with a little of the olive oil, then fold them in half. Stack them one on top of the other on another non-stick baking tray.

3. Heat the remaining olive oil in a frying pan over a medium heat. Add the ground coriander, fennel seeds, spring onions, cumin seeds and garlic, and stir-fry until the spices are toasted and fragrant. Add the chilli powder and the tomatoes (you may need to do this in two batches) and cook for 1–2 minutes, being careful not to break up the tomato slices. Pour off any cooking juices and reserve.

4. Arrange the tomatoes on the pastry stack, placing them at least 5mm from the edge of the pastry. Set the baking tray on top of the hot tray in the oven and cook for 15–20 minutes, until the pastry is crisp and golden.

5. Drizzle any reserved tomato juices over the tart and serve.

ACTIVE

CHINESE BEEF & PEPPER WRAPS

SERVES 4

- 1 tablespoon sesame oil
- 1 medium carrot, cut into very thin strips (or strips cut with a potato peeler)
- 4 spring onions, sliced thinly lengthways
- 2 red peppers, deseeded and very thinly sliced
- 1 garlic clove, peeled and crushed
- 2cm piece of fresh root ginger, peeled and grated
- 300g good-quality steak beef, cut into thin strips and all visible fat removed
- 2 tablespoons soy sauce
- 4 wholewheat wraps

This dish will feel like a treat but it is incredibly light. Compare this to any processed Chinese food you used to eat before taking the Bikini Promise... no chemicals, additives or preservatives, just healthy ingredients made in the tastiest way.

1. Heat the sesame oil in a wok over a high heat, then add all the vegetables, garlic and ginger and stir-fry for 4 minutes.

2. Next, add the beef strips and the soy sauce to the vegetables and stir-fry for a further 2–3 minutes.

3. Remove from the heat and serve the beef and vegetables immediately, wrapped in the wholewheat wraps, while trying not to dribble juice down your chin!

The science is simple. If you eat less and move more you WILL lose weight.

ACTIVE

MINI NO-FRY FALAFELS

V

SERVES 4

2 x 400g cans chickpeas, drained and rinsed
2 garlic cloves, peeled and crushed
1 teaspoon ground cumin
1 teaspoon ground coriander
1 green chilli, deseeded and finely chopped
2 tablespoons chopped fresh coriander
1 small egg, lightly beaten
2 tablespoons plain flour
sea salt and freshly ground black pepper, to taste
4 wholemeal pitta breads, to serve

FOR THE SALAD:
100g red cabbage, finely shredded
1 carrot, peeled and coarsely grated
½ cucumber, peeled and cut into fine matchsticks
1 small red onion, peeled and thinly sliced

FOR THE DRESSING:
2 tablespoons low-fat Greek yogurt
1 teaspoon dried mint

If you have never tried falafels, give these delicious mini ones a try. They are great to make ahead of time and take to work as a packed lunch. They are quite filling, so remember to listen to your body and let it tell you when it's had enough!

1. Put the chickpeas in a blender or the bowl of a food-processor and process until smooth. Add the garlic, cumin and ground coriander and process again until well combined. Add the chilli, fresh coriander, egg and 1 tablespoon of the flour and process again briefly. Season to taste. Transfer to a bowl, cover and chill for about 30 minutes to firm up the mixture.

2. Meanwhile, prepare the salad. Combine the cabbage, carrot, cucumber and onion in a bowl.

3. Preheat the oven to 200°C/gas mark 6 and line a baking tray with parchment paper.

4. Dust your hands with the remaining flour and shape the chilled chickpea mixture into eight patties.

5. Place the falafel patties on the lined tray and bake for 10–15 minutes, until heated through and golden brown.

6. Meanwhile, warm the pitta breads in a toaster or under the grill, and whisk the dressing ingredients together. Cut a slit lengthways in the side of each warmed pitta bread to form a pocket. Fill each pitta pocket with two of the falafel balls, sliced, a little salad, and a drizzle of the dressing.

LIGHT

ACTIVE WITH RICE

HEALTHY CHICKEN KORMA

SERVES 2

2 tablespoons extra virgin olive oil
2 skinless chicken breasts, cut into chunks
1 onion, peeled and finely chopped
1 tablespoon curry powder (level of heat dependent on how spicy you like it!)
1 tablespoon ground almonds
1 tablespoon tomato purée
1 garlic clove, crushed
4 tablespoons low-fat crème fraîche
a small handful of whole blanched almonds, to serve

FOR THE SALSA:
1 fresh, ripe pineapple, peeled, core removed and flesh finely chopped
½ red onion, finely sliced
1 green chilli, deseeded and finely chopped
1 red chilli, deseeded and finely chopped
a handful of fresh coriander, chopped
a handful of fresh mint leaves, chopped
juice of 2 limes

The pineapple salsa with this chicken korma will blow your mind! The recipe will make more than two portions, but the rest will keep in the fridge for three days.

1. Heat the olive oil in a non-stick saucepan over a medium heat, then add the chicken and onion and fry for 4–5 minutes.

2. Add the curry powder and stir well, letting the spices release their aroma in the heat of the pan.

3. Now, add four tablespoons of water, the ground almonds, tomato purée, garlic and crème fraîche.

4. Let the mixture simmer for 5–10 minutes, covered, until the chicken is cooked through, adding a little extra water if the sauce becomes too thick, then remove from the heat.

5. To make the salsa, mix all the ingredients together in a large bowl with the lime juice.

6. Serve the curry and salsa with the almonds and a small portion of basmati rice or a toasted wholemeal wrap (instead of high fat poppadoms).

MOROCCAN BUTTERNUT COUSCOUS

SERVES 4

100g couscous
250g very lean beef mince
1 large onion, finely chopped
2 tablespoons tomato purée
2 tablespoons Moroccan spice mix (see below)
400g butternut squash, peeled, deseeded and cut into small chunks
2 courgettes, thinly sliced
100g spring cabbage or baby spinach leaves
low-fat crème fraîche, to serve
lemon wedges, to serve

FOR THE SPICE MIX:
5 teaspoons ground nutmeg
5 teaspoons ground cumin
5 teaspoons ground coriander
2½ teaspoons ground allspice
2½ teaspoons ground ginger
1 teaspoon cayenne pepper
1 teaspoon ground cinnamon

Because you are not relying on fat and sugar to give your food flavour, the Moroccan spices in this dish do that job perfectly.

1. Put the couscous in a heatproof bowl and cover with boiling water, according to the packet instructions. Cover with clingfilm and set aside until the liquid is absorbed. Remove the clingfilm and fluff up with a fork.

2. Place a deep, non-stick frying pan over a high heat and dry-fry the mince (no oil needed) for 5 minutes until browned, breaking it up with a wooden spoon.

3. Add the onion, tomato purée and spice mix to the beef and cook for a further 3 minutes.

4. Add the butternut squash and 250ml of water and bring to the boil. Reduce the heat to medium and simmer for 3–4 minutes, then add the courgettes and spring cabbage. Simmer, uncovered, for a further 4–5 minutes or until sauce has reduced and the vegetables are tender.

5. Divide the couscous between four serving bowls. Top with the meat and vegetable mixture and serve with a dollop of low-fat crème fraîche and lemon wedges.

TIP: In this recipe I use a Moroccan spice mix, which you can find at most large supermarkets. You could also make your own by simply combining the ingredients and keeping it in an airtight box.

ACTIVE

LIGHT PUFF PASTRY PIZZA

(V)

SERVES 2

1 320g packet ready-rolled 'light' puff pastry
2 tablespoons tomato purée
½ onion, peeled and sliced (or use frozen)
½ red pepper, deseeded and sliced (or use frozen)
a small handful of sliced button mushrooms
a small handful of drained, canned sweetcorn (or thawed, frozen sweetcorn)
50g mature Cheddar cheese, grated
a pinch of dried oregano

Shop-bought light puff pastry makes this pizza very quick to make, and plenty of colourful vegetables add nutrition, with a little mature Cheddar cheese giving the dish extra flavour without adding too much fat.

1. Preheat the oven to 220°C/gas mark 7 and line a baking tray with baking parchment.

2. Unroll the pastry and place it on the baking parchment. With a small, sharp knife, score a 1cm border around the edge of the pastry, being careful not to cut right through the pastry.

3. Spread the tomato purée all over the pastry, within the scored border.

4. Sprinkle over the sliced vegetables – you can add anything you like as long as it's healthy (so no fat-loaded salami!).

5. Scatter over the grated cheese and dried oregano.

6. Bake in the oven for about 20 minutes, until risen and golden.

Remember, if it doesn't have a health benefit, don't eat it!

TEN WAYS WITH CHICKEN

LIGHT

OVEN-BAKED CRISPY CHICKEN

SERVES 4

½ cup ground almonds
¼ cup wholewheat flour
½ teaspoon paprika
½ teaspoon garlic granules or 2 crushed garlic cloves
½ teaspoon English mustard powder
½ teaspoon celery salt
freshly ground black pepper, to taste
2 teaspoons extra virgin olive oil
4 large egg whites
450g chicken breast pieces
summer salad, to serve

Oh yes my friends, it is possible to get the taste of the deep south... and not have it served in a red bucket! I am giving you cup measurements here for some of the ingredients as this is not science and approximate measurements will do the job fine!

1. Preheat the oven to 200°C/gas mark 6 and line a baking tray with foil. Set a wire rack on the baking tray and brush it with oil.

2. Put the ground almonds, flour, paprika, garlic granules or cloves, mustard powder, celery salt and pepper in a medium-sized shallow bowl and stir until the ingredients are thoroughly mixed. Add the olive oil to the dry mixture and stir until roughly combined. Set aside.

3. Whisk the egg whites for a couple of minutes in a shallow dish until little bubbles form. Dip the chicken pieces one at a time in the frothy egg whites, then dip them in the almond mixture, ensuring they're well coated.

4. Place the coated chicken pieces on the wire rack and bake for 20–25 minutes until golden brown, crisp and no longer pink in the middle.

5. Serve with a big summer salad.

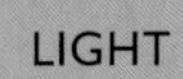

MOROCCAN CHICKEN WITH ROASTED VEG

SERVES 4

2 teaspoons harissa paste
150g low-fat Greek yogurt
freshly ground black pepper, to taste
800g chicken drumsticks, skin removed
1 red pepper, deseeded and sliced
1 green pepper, deseeded and sliced
1 yellow pepper, deseeded and sliced
1 aubergine, cut into 3cm dice
6 shallots, peeled and halved
75g green olives stuffed with hot pimento (or ordinary olives if you don't have stuffed)
2 tablespoons extra virgin olive oil
salad, to serve

This is a brilliant dish to feed friends and family when they all decide to pop over on a sunny day. Just increase the quantities and serve with extra roasted vegetables. You'll wonder why you haven't been eating like this your whole life!

1. Preheat the oven to 200°C/gas mark 6.

2. Mix together the harissa paste and half the yogurt in a large bowl, season with plenty of black pepper and add the chicken drumsticks, stirring to coat them evenly. Cover with clingfilm and leave to marinate in the fridge for 30 minutes.

3. Place all the vegetables, shallots and olives in a roasting tin and drizzle with the olive oil, then shake the tin from side to side to ensure that the vegetables are well coated. Place the chicken on top of the vegetables, spooning over any marinade left in the bowl.

4. Bake for 30–40 minutes, or until the chicken is thoroughly cooked. Check by piercing the drumstick at its thickest point down to the bone – the juices should run clear, with no pink flesh. Serve with the remaining Greek yogurt and a salad.

Cut out alcohol until you have reached your target weight.

WEST INDIAN CHICKEN KEBABS

SERVES 4

I teaspoon ground cumin
I teaspoon ground allspice
I onion, peeled and chopped
I garlic clove, peeled and crushed
grated zest and juice of 2 limes
a handful of parsley, chopped
I red chilli, deseeded and finely chopped
Icm piece of fresh root ginger, peeled and grated
2 tablespoons rice wine vinegar (or white wine vinegar)
I tablespoon runny honey
4 skinless chicken breasts, cut into 2cm cubes

These kebabs will blow your mind! When you are not relying on fat, sugar and salt to give your food flavour, spice mixes and an extra kick from red chillies and ginger really give dishes a boost.

These kebabs go really well with coconut rice and a green salad.

When you buy fresh chillies, wash them, dry them, chop them in half and freeze them in a little freezer bag. Then, when a recipe calls for half a chilli, you will have it to hand. They take just minutes to defrost at room temperature.

I. Start by making the marinade. Place all the ingredients, except the chicken, in a food-processor with 2 tablespoons of water and blend until thoroughly combined.

2. Place the cubes of chicken in a non-metallic bowl, then pour the marinade over the chicken and mix to coat it thoroughly. Cover and leave to marinate in the fridge for at least an hour, or overnight if you can.

3. When you are ready to cook the kebabs, preheat the oven to 200°C/gas mark 6.

4. Remove the marinated chicken from the fridge and thread the pieces onto pre-soaked wooden skewers. Transfer to a roasting tin and bake for I hour, or until crisp and the meat is thoroughly cooked. Serve the kebabs with any juices from the roasting tray poured over.

LIGHT

ACTIVE WITH RICE

SPANISH CHICKEN

SERVES 4

- 10 skinless, boneless chicken thighs
- 2 tablespoons extra virgin olive oil
- 2 onions, peeled and chopped
- 3 garlic cloves, peeled and chopped
- 125ml dry sherry (or red wine)
- 200ml low-salt chicken stock
- 1 tablespoon dried thyme
- 2 tablespoons pine nuts
- 50g raisins
- a handful of flat-leaf parsley, chopped, to serve

I've adapted this full-flavoured Spanish dish to make it healthier than the original. The most important thing is to cook the fat out of the chicken and discard it. Cooking with sherry makes this dish authentically Spanish – yum! If you want to stretch this meal to feed more people, add some dried mixed lentils and extra chicken stock to bulk it out.

1. Preheat the oven to 200°C/gas mark 6.

2. Place the chicken thighs in a shallow, non-stick baking tray and roast for 30–35 minutes until cooked through and all the fat has been released. The thighs should have gently browned on the edges. Drain away the fat and blot the thighs on kitchen paper to remove any remaining fat, then set aside.

3. Heat the olive oil in a large non-stick frying pan over a medium heat, and cook the onions for 3–4 minutes, stirring, then add the garlic and cook for a further 3–4 minutes.

3. Add the sherry or wine, then simmer for 3–5 minutes until lovely and syrupy (add some lentils and extra chicken stock at this point, if you want the dish to feed more people).

5. Put the roast chicken thighs into the pan, tip in the stock, thyme, pine nuts and raisins, cover, then cook gently over a low heat for 20–30 minutes until the sauce has reduced and the chicken is lovely and tender.

5. Scatter with the chopped parsley and serve with rice (for an Active dish).

ACTIVE

ITALIAN CHICKEN & TOMATO RISOTTO

SERVES 4

1 tablespoon extra virgin olive oil
1 large onion or 4 shallots, peeled and finely chopped
100g cherry tomatoes, halved
1 garlic clove, peeled and crushed
500ml tomato juice
1 low-salt chicken stock cube
200g Arborio rice
1 tablespoon tomato purée
a large handful of cooked chicken, torn
juice of ½ lemon
1 tablespoon chilled unsalted butter
a handful of fresh basil leaves, torn
2 tablespoons grated Parmesan, to serve
freshly ground black pepper, to taste
a few fresh basil leaves, to garnish
lemon wedges, to serve

This recipe calls for cooked chicken, so it's perfect for the Monday after a Sunday roast. If you don't have cooked chicken to hand, roast a couple of breasts in the oven, then roughly tear the cooked meat.

1. Heat the olive oil in a large non-stick saucepan over a medium heat. Add the onions or shallots, cherry tomatoes and garlic and sauté gently for 10 minutes, or until softened but not coloured.

2. Put the tomato juice and stock cube in another pan over a medium heat and bring to simmering point.

3. Add the rice to the onion mixture and cook, stirring frequently, for 1–2 minutes, until the rice becomes transparent.

4. Add a small ladleful of hot tomato juice to the rice mixture and stir continuously until all the juice has been absorbed. Repeat, stirring after each ladleful of juice has been added, and cook for 15–20 minutes until the rice is tender and has a creamy consistency, adding some water if necessary.

5. When the rice is cooked, stir the tomato purée, cooked chicken, lemon juice, butter and torn basil leaves into the rice and mix to combine and heat through.

6. Serve garnished with a sprinkle of Parmesan, freshly ground black pepper, basil leaves and with lemon wedges on the side.

ACTIVE

LEMON CHICKEN ESCALOPES

SERVES 4

FOR THE CHICKEN ESCALOPES:
4 skinless chicken breasts
250g brown breadcrumbs (stale bread whizzed up in a food-processor is ideal)
1 tablespoon mixed dried herbs
freshly ground black pepper, to taste
juice and grated zest of 1 unwaxed lemon
1 teaspoon garlic granules
½ teaspoon smoked paprika
2 tablespoons extra virgin olive oil
2 eggs, beaten

FOR THE TOMATO SALSA:
225g ripe vine tomatoes, finely diced
1 red pepper, deseeded and finely diced
½ green chilli, deseeded and finely chopped
1 red chilli, deseeded and finely chopped
2 teaspoons balsamic vinegar
1 tablespoon chopped fresh chives
1 tablespoon chopped fresh coriander

To save time, you can chop all the salsa ingredients together in a food-processor – just use the pulse button until you have the right consistency.

1. Preheat the oven to 200°C/gas mark 6 and line a baking tray with baking parchment.

2. For the chicken escalopes, sandwich each chicken breast between two sheets of clingfilm. Using a rolling pin, bash each breast until it is about 1cm thick. Discard the clingfilm and set the chicken aside.

3. In a large, shallow dish, mix together the breadcrumbs, herbs, black pepper, lemon zest, garlic granules and smoked paprika. Add the olive oil and lemon juice, to dampen the mixture (though it should still resemble breadcrumbs).

4. Place the beaten eggs in a separate bowl and dip a chicken escalope in the egg to cover it, then dredge it through the breadcrumb mixture, to give it a good coating. Place the coated escalope on the prepared baking tray, and repeat the dipping and dredging process with the remaining chicken escalopes.

5. Bake the chicken escalopes in the oven for 15–20 minutes, until cooked through and crispy.

6. To make the salsa, mix all the ingredients together in a bowl. Season to taste.

ACTIVE

BOMBAY POTATO & CHICKEN WRAPS

SERVES 4

- 1 tablespoon extra virgin olive oil
- 1 large red onion, peeled and finely chopped
- 3 garlic cloves, peeled and crushed
- 200g skinless, boneless chicken thigh fillets, sliced
- 3 tablespoons tikka curry paste
- 400g can chopped tomatoes
- 2 large potatoes, washed and cut into 2cm cubes
- freshly ground black pepper, to taste
- 250g frozen peas
- 8 wholemeal wraps or chapattis
- 140g low-fat Greek yogurt or low-fat crème fraîche

Eating for health does not mean you have to forego flavour. This is a low-fat, high-nutrient dish that is perfectly balanced and tastes much better than any dodgy takeaway!

1. Heat the olive oil in a large non-stick frying pan over a medium heat, then add the onion and fry for a few minutes until softened. Add the garlic and stir for a further minute, then add the chicken and cook, stirring, until browned.

2. Stir in the curry paste, tomatoes, potatoes and half a can of water. Season well with plenty of black pepper, then cover and simmer for about 20 minutes, until the potatoes are just cooked.

3. Remove the lid and simmer for a further 10–15 minutes, until the liquid has reduced and the sauce is sticking to the potatoes and chicken. Stir in the peas and cook until the peas are cooked, then serve with warmed wraps or chapattis, and yogurt.

CHARGRILLED CHICKEN WITH AVOCADO PESTO

SERVES 4

250g thin-stemmed broccoli, trimmed and cut into bite-sized florets
1 red onion, peeled and thinly sliced
2 tablespoons extra virgin olive oil
3 skinless chicken breasts
freshly ground black pepper, to taste
100g watercress
2 raw beetroot, peeled and cut into thin strips (julienned), or grated
50g walnut pieces

FOR THE AVOCADO PESTO:
a handful of fresh basil leaves
1 ripe avocado, halved, pitted and peeled
1 garlic clove, peeled and crushed
25g walnut halves, crumbled
1 tablespoon extra virgin olive oil
grated zest and juice of 1 lemon

You see... salads no longer mean soggy lettuce and watery cucumber. All the ingredients in this salad will top you up and feed your taste buds.

1. Bring a large pan of water to the boil, add the broccoli florets and blanch for 2 minutes, then drain and refresh in cold water.

2. Put a griddle pan or non-stick frying pan over a medium heat. Toss the blanched broccoli and sliced onion in 1 tablespoon of the olive oil and griddle or fry for 2–3 minutes, until slightly charred. Set aside the vegetables, but keep the pan on the heat.

3. Brush the chicken breasts with the remaining oil and season with black pepper. Griddle for 3–4 minutes on each side, or until cooked through. Remove and leave to cool, then cut into bite-sized pieces.

4. To make the pesto, pop the basil leaves and avocado into a food-processor. Add the garlic, walnuts, olive oil, 1 tablespoon of the lemon juice and the lemon zest and 2–3 tablespoons of cold water. Blend until smooth, then transfer to a small serving dish.

5. Mix together the watercress, broccoli and onion in a large salad bowl. Then, add the chicken, beetroot and the remaining lemon juice. Top with the walnut pieces and serve with the avocado pesto.

LIGHT

CHICKEN IN A CREAMY TARRAGON SAUCE

SERVES 4

- 1 tablespoon extra virgin olive oil
- 4 skinless chicken breasts, whole
- 1 large onion, peeled and finely chopped
- 2 garlic cloves, peeled and crushed
- 350ml low-salt chicken stock
- a small bunch of fresh tarragon, chopped (or 3 teaspoons dried tarragon)
- 120g asparagus spears, trimmed
- 120g French green beans, trimmed
- 4 tablespoons low-fat crème fraîche
- brown rice, to serve

Fresh tarragon gives this dish the most delicious flavour. If asparagus isn't available you can substitute it with broccoli. Another easy dish to tempt your taste buds while eating healthily.

1. Heat the olive oil in a large non-stick frying pan over a medium heat, then add the chicken, onion and garlic and fry for 5–6 minutes, stirring, until the chicken is lightly browned on both sides.

2. Pour over the stock, add half of the chopped tarragon and simmer gently for 5 minutes.

3. Add the asparagus spears and the beans and cook for a further 3 minutes, then stir in the crème fraîche and remaining tarragon and heat through.

4. Serve with a small portion of brown rice.

The Bikini Promise will ensure you get the body you deserve.

CHICKEN MEATBALLS WITH BEAN CHILLI

SERVES 4

FOR THE MEATBALLS:
- 1 large carrot, finely chopped
- 1 onion roughly chopped
- 2 garlic cloves, peeled
- ½ red chilli deseeded (or 1 teaspoon dried chilli flakes)
- 500g lean chicken or turkey mince
- 20g fresh breadcrumbs
- 1 free-range egg
- 1 tablespoon dried Italian herbs
- ½ teaspoon ground cinnamon

FOR THE BEAN CHILLI:
- 1 tablespoon extra virgin olive oil
- 1 large onion, finely chopped
- 2 garlic cloves, crushed
- 1 green pepper, deseeded and diced
- 1 teaspoon ground cumin
- dash of Worcestershire sauce
- 3 teaspoons chipotle chilli paste
- 300ml low-salt chicken or vegetable stock
- 400g can chopped tomatoes
- 400g can black-eyed beans (or red kidney beans), drained and rinsed
- green salad, to serve

Make friends with your local butcher and ask him to organise you some turkey mince if it's not readily available in your supermarket. Of course, this can also be suitable for vegetarians, simply serve without the meatballs.

1. Preheat the oven to 200°C/gas mark 6, and cover a baking tray with baking parchment.

2. To make the meatballs, pop the carrot, onion, garlic and chilli in a food-processor and blitz for a few seconds until finely minced. Transfer to a bowl and combine with the remaining ingredients, using your hands to mix everything together.

3. Shape the mixture into meatballs the size of ping-pong balls and place on the prepared baking tray.

4. Bake for 30 minutes, then check the meatballs are no longer pink in the middle. Continue cooking for 5 minutes if they aren't cooked through.

5. While the meatballs are baking, make the black bean chilli. Heat the olive oil in a large non-stick frying pan over a medium heat, add the onion and cook gently for 4–5 minutes, until softened.

6. Add the garlic, green pepper, cumin, Worcestershire sauce, chipotle chilli paste, stock, tomatoes and beans. Bring to the boil, then reduce the heat and simmer for 15 minutes.

7. When you are ready to serve, put a big scoop of the black bean chilli in a bowl and serve the meatballs on top, with a big green salad on the side.

TEN WAYS WITH EGGS

ACTIVE

SPINACH & SWEET POTATO FRITTATA

V

SERVES 2–3

2 tablespoons olive oil
1 small onion, peeled and finely chopped
½ sweet potato, peeled and cut into small chunks
1 garlic clove, peeled and crushed
freshly ground black pepper, to taste
3 handfuls of baby spinach leaves
8 cherry tomatoes, halved
4 free-range eggs, lightly beaten
a handful of fresh parsley, chopped
green salad, to serve

Both spinach and sweet potato are what I would class as superfoods. This means they are nutrient dense and you don't have to eat a truckload of them to get all the goodness you need. When you are on the Bikini Promise and making healthier changes, sometimes speed is still important. This is a wonderful dish that is quick to make, and it will keep cold for lunch the following day.

1. Preheat the oven to 180°C/gas mark 4.

2. Heat the olive oil in an ovenproof frying pan over a medium heat, add the onion and sauté for 3–4 minutes, until softened.

3. Add the sweet potato chunks and continue to fry for a further 3–4 minutes, or until the sweet potato is tender and cooked through. Add the crushed garlic, black pepper, spinach and cherry tomatoes, then pour in the beaten eggs.

4. Cook on the hob for 3–4 minutes, then pop the frying pan into the oven and bake for 3–4 minutes, or until the egg is set. Serve with a sprinkling of fresh chopped parsley with a green salad on the side.

ACTIVE

(V)

SPICY BAKED POTATO WITH AN EGGY MIDDLE

SERVES 1

- 1 large baking potato, scrubbed
- 1 spring onion, finely sliced
- dash of Tabasco sauce
- 2 tablespoons low-fat crème fraîche
- 1 large free-range egg
- 20g mature Cheddar cheese, grated

This is another super-quick, healthy recipe, which I would serve with a mixed salad. Although the cooking time is quite long, the preparation time is no more than five minutes, so you can get on with other things while it's cooking.

1. Preheat the oven to 200°C/gas mark 6.

2. Prick the potato skin several times, place directly on the oven shelf, and bake for 40–50 minutes, until just cooked through.

3. Once cooked, take the baked potato out of the oven and carefully cut a slice off the top (being careful not to burn your hands).

4. Scoop out the cooked potato and put it in a bowl with the spring onion, Tabasco and crème fraîche. Mix well, then return the potato to its skin, make a hollow in the top, and crack the egg into the hollow.

5. Scatter the cheese over the top and return to the oven for a further 8–10 minutes, or until the egg is baked to your liking and the cheese is melted and browned.

Cut out ALL processed and take-away food.

ACTIVE

KICKING SCRAMBLED EGGS

V

SERVES 3

- 1 teaspoon olive oil
- 1 small onion, or a couple of spring onions, peeled and very finely chopped
- ½ green chilli, deseeded and very finely chopped, or a pinch of chilli powder
- pinch of ground turmeric
- pinch of curry powder
- 1 tomato, roughly chopped
- 6 free-range eggs, lightly beaten
- 3 slices whole-nutty bread, to serve

Who doesn't love scrambled eggs on toast? There's something about a plate of warm scrambled eggs that is both filling and wholesome, and if you serve this with a slice of chunky granary or whole-nutty bread and some baked tomatoes, you have a complete meal made in minutes.

1. Heat the olive oil in a non-stick frying pan, add the onion and fry until softened, then add the chilli, turmeric and curry powder and stir for a minute, before adding the tomato.

2. Stir the eggs into the pan so they scramble with the onion mixture, stirring until the eggs are cooked to your liking. Serve immediately on slices of toasted whole-nutty bread.

ACTIVE

NEW SEASON SALAD NIÇOISE

SERVES 2

200g new potatoes, washed and thickly sliced
2 medium free-range eggs
100g green beans, trimmed
1 romaine lettuce heart, leaves separated and washed
10 cherry tomatoes, halved
6 anchovies in olive oil, drained well
197g can tuna steak in spring water, drained
3 tablespoons low-fat crème fraîche
freshly ground black pepper, to taste
2 teaspoons capers

New potatoes bring a real taste of summer to a meal. Full of vitamins and nicely filling, this dish will be a staple on the Bikini Promise plan.

1. Bring a large pan of water to the boil. Add the sliced potatoes and the eggs, and cook for 7 minutes.

2. Scoop the eggs out of the pan and set aside to cool, then tip in the green beans and cook for 4 minutes.

3. Drain the potatoes and beans and put them in a colander with the eggs, under cold running water, until cool. Leave to drain.

4. Peel the eggs and cut them into quarters. Arrange the lettuce leaves in two shallow bowls. Scatter over the beans, potatoes, tomatoes and egg quarters. Pat the anchovies with kitchen paper to absorb the excess oil and place them on top.

5. Flake the tuna into chunks and scatter over the salad. Mix the low-fat crème fraîche with black pepper and the capers. Drizzle this dressing over the salad and serve.

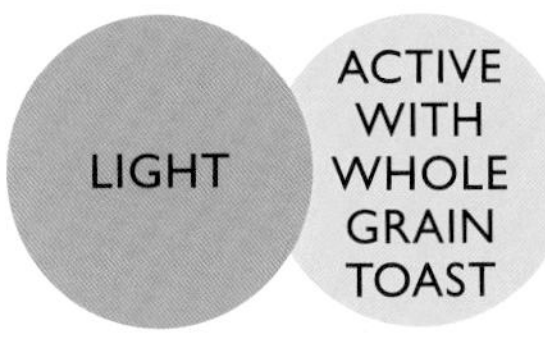

SPINACH & EGGS

V

SERVES 1–2

2 large free-range eggs
1 tablespoon olive oil
1 garlic clove, peeled and crushed
1 teaspoon lemon juice
200g spinach, washed and drained
freshly ground black pepper, to taste

This dish makes a wonderful healthy and filling breakfast or brunch, but it is also perfect for a quick, light supper. You don't absorb the cholesterol from eggs – this is an old wives' tale and doctors now recommend that an egg a day gives you essential healthy proteins.

1. Crack both the eggs onto a plate, being careful not to break the yolks.

2. Bring a pan of water to a rolling boil and carefully slide the eggs in. Place a lid on the pan and turn off the heat. Leave the eggs to cook in the hot water for 3 minutes.

3. Meanwhile, warm the olive oil in a saucepan over a medium heat. Add the crushed garlic and lemon juice.

4. Using a slotted spoon, remove the poached eggs and set them aside on a plate.

5. Add the spinach to the warm olive oil and lemon juice, stir well and heat through for 1–2 minutes, or until the spinach has wilted.

6. To serve, pop the poached eggs on top of a bed of spinach.

ACTIVE

(V)

LOW-FAT EGG & WATERCRESS OPEN SANDWICH

SERVES 2

2 free-range eggs
3 tablespoons low-fat crème fraîche
½ green pepper, deseeded and finely diced
freshly ground black pepper, to taste
2 slices rye bread
1 large bunch of watercress

A delicious British summer classic made in a healthier way. Sometimes the oldies are the goodies!

1. Hard-boil the eggs for 10 minutes. Peel them and place in a small bowl. Roughly crush them using the back of a fork. Add the crème fraîche, diced green pepper and some freshly ground black pepper, to taste, then mix well.

2. Divide the egg mixture between the two unbuttered slices of rye bread, piling watercress on top of each open sandwich.

ACTIVE

(V)

SPANISH OMELETTE

SERVES 4

2 potatoes, peeled and cut into 2cm cubes
1 tablespoon olive oil
1 green pepper, deseeded and thinly sliced
1 red pepper, deseeded and thinly sliced
1 small onion, finely chopped
1 garlic clove, finely chopped
6 free-range eggs, lightly beaten
4 tablespoons grated mature Cheddar cheese

This basic recipe works brilliantly, but you can add any leftovers you have to hand. So raid the fridge and be adventurous. It can be eaten hot on the day it's cooked, or cold the next day.

1. Cook the cubed potatoes in boiling water until soft but still retaining their shape. Drain.

2. Heat the olive oil in an ovenproof frying pan over a medium heat, then add the potatoes, peppers, onion and garlic. Cook for about 10 minutes, stirring, until all the vegetables are soft and golden brown.

3. Stir in the beaten eggs and reduce the heat. Cook gently until the omelette is lightly set. Sprinkle over the grated cheese and transfer the frying pan to the grill, until the cheese is melted and golden brown.

ACTIVE

MINI MEXICAN EGGS

SERVES 4

- 2 tablespoons extra virgin olive oil
- 1 medium onion, peeled and finely sliced
- 4 lean rashers of bacon, trimmed of all visible fat and chopped
- 2 garlic cloves, peeled and crushed
- 2 x 400g cans chopped tomatoes
- 400g can butter beans
- freshly ground black pepper, to taste
- 4 preserved jalapeños, deseeded and chopped
- dash of Tabasco sauce, to taste
- 4 free-range eggs

A simple, fun and filling breakfast dish with a bit of a kick!

1. Preheat the oven to 200°C/gas mark 6.

2. Heat the oil in a large non-stick frying pan over a medium heat. Add the sliced onion and fry, stirring, for 4–5 minutes until soft.

3. Stir in the bacon, garlic, chopped tomatoes and butter beans, then season with black pepper and add the jalapeños and Tabasco sauce. Stir to combine and simmer, uncovered, over a low heat for 10–15 minutes.

4. Divide the mixture between four ovenproof ramekins, transfer the ramekins to a baking tray and bake in the oven for 15 minutes, until bubbling.

5. Carefully remove the ramekins from the oven and make a well in the sauce in the middle of each ramekin.

6. Crack an egg into each well and pop the ramekins back in the oven for a final 6–7 minutes, until the eggs are set.

ACTIVE

V

TAP TAP EGGS & WHOLE-NUTTY 'BREADSTICKS'

SERVES 3

3 large free-range eggs
whole-nutty bread

Now you might think I've lost my marbles putting this as a recipe in the Bikini Promise, but I don't think I have! The humble boiled egg is a complete meal in a shell, and we seem to have forgotten some of these very simple pleasures in life.

We've been calling boiled eggs 'Tap Tap Eggs' in my house since our children were tiny. They make the perfect breakfast: filling, nutritious and packed with great protein that will keep you full up until lunchtime (and they are perfect for a quick lunch or tea, too!),

So, just in case you have not mastered the art, to boil an egg perfectly you need to:

Start with eggs that are at room temperature.

For a soft-boiled egg: lower the egg into gently simmering water with a slotted spoon. Allow 3½ minutes for a medium-sized egg and 4 minutes for a large egg. The yolk will be runny and the white just set. Cook for a further minute if you like your soft-boiled eggs a little firmer.
For a hard-boiled egg: place the egg in cold water and bring up to the boil. Once the water is gently boiling, set the timer for between 7–10 minutes, depending on how well cooked you like your eggs. The longer you boil the egg, the firmer it will be.

Once cooked, plunge the eggs into plenty of cold water for 1 minute. Drain and cover with more cold water. This stops the eggs cooking further.

In the Bikini Promise, don't assume you always have to have your egg with bread, although it's great to have a slice of whole-nutty bread (see page p27) at breakfast time to set you up for the day. Instead of good old-fashioned toast 'soldiers', cut your bread into thinner strips and toast as 'breadsticks'.

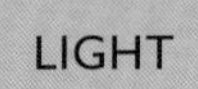

V

SUMMER SLIM EGGS EN COCOTTE

SERVES 4

I tablespoon olive oil, plus extra for greasing
½ medium onion, peeled and finely diced (it's handy to have frozen chopped onion to hand, for recipes like this!)
I garlic clove, peeled and crushed
3 large tomatoes, finely chopped
freshly ground black pepper, to taste
4 free-range eggs
Tabasco sauce, to taste
2 tablespoons snipped chives
whole-nutty bread, to serve

Eggs are one of the best self-contained foods on the planet. Everything you need all wrapped up in a nice protective shell. By adding onions, tomatoes and garlic to this dish, you are increasing the health benefits massively. This is filling, tasty and super healthy. Perfect to set you up for an active day.

1. Preheat the oven to 180°C/gas mark 4.

2. Start by making the tomato sauce. Heat the olive oil in a heavy-based frying pan over a medium heat, then add the onion and garlic and cook for 2 minutes. Add the chopped tomatoes and season with black pepper. Simmer for 15 minutes, or until thickened.

3. Meanwhile, grease four ramekins with a little olive oil on a piece of kitchen paper.

4. Crack one egg into each ramekin, taking care not to break the yolks, then pour the tomato sauce around the outside of each egg so that the yolk is still visible.

5. Add a dash of Tabasco sauce, to taste, and sprinkle with snipped chives.

6. Place the ramekins in a deep baking dish and pour enough hot water into the dish to come halfway up the sides of the ramekins. Bake for 10–12 minutes, or until the egg whites are set.

7. Serve with toasted fingers of whole-nutty bread, lightly buttered.

FISH SUPPER

ACTIVE

HERB-CRUSTED FISH WITH GARLIC MINI ROASTIES

SERVES 4

600g small, whole waxy new potatoes, still in their skins (cut any large ones in half)
extra virgin olive oil
1 teaspoon celery salt
1 teaspoon garlic granules
2 tablespoons ground almonds
2 tablespoons snipped fresh herbs (such as parsley, dill, chives and tarragon)
freshly ground black pepper, to taste
4 firm white fish fillets, cod or haddock are good

The beauty of this dish is its simplicity. You just need some mixed green vegetables to make a balanced meal, and frozen vegetables would be fine.

1. Preheat the oven to 200°C/gas mark 6.

2. Brush the new potatoes with olive oil so they are glistening, but not drowning. Sprinkle the potatoes with the celery salt and garlic granules and place in a single layer on a baking tray. Bake for 35–45 minutes until golden and cooked through.

3. Meanwhile, put the ground almonds and mixed fresh herbs in a small bowl. Stir in a tablespoon of olive oil and season with black pepper.

4. Put the fish fillets on a greased baking tray and spread a quarter of the herb mixture on top of each piece of fish. Bake for about 12 minutes until cooked through, then serve with the mini roasties and a big pile of vegetables.

Remember – fast for 12 hours at night.

ACTIVE

SATAY PRAWNS WITH SALAD & PITTA BREAD

SERVES 4

2 tablespoons crunchy peanut butter
1 teaspoon soy sauce
1 tablespoon dark brown sugar
2 garlic cloves, peeled and crushed
2 teaspoons mild curry powder
1 teaspoon Chinese five-spice powder
340g large cooked and peeled prawns
1 tablespoon extra virgin olive oil
1 onion, peeled and sliced
100g mangetout (or frozen peas, defrosted)
100g baby sweetcorn, sliced
200g beansprouts
salad and pitta bread strips, to serve

Buy wholemeal pitta bread and keep it in the freezer. That way, you can take one out when you need it and pop it straight into the toaster!

1. In a large bowl, combine the peanut butter, soy sauce, sugar, garlic, curry powder and five-spice powder, then add the prawns and stir to combine.

2. Heat the olive oil in a large non-stick frying pan over a high heat, then add the onion and cook for 3–4 minutes, stirring, until it starts to soften.

3. Now add the mangetout and sweetcorn, with a tablespoon of water, and continue stir-frying for a further couple of minutes. Add the prawn mixture and beansprouts and cook for a further 2–3 minutes until all the ingredients are blended and piping hot.

4. Serve with a big fresh salad and toasted wholemeal pitta bread strips.

TERIYAKI TUNA WITH MANGETOUT & BABY CORN

SERVES 4

- 4 fresh tuna steaks (around 600g in total)
- 2 tablespoons teriyaki sauce
- 1 teaspoon garlic granules
- 4 blocks (about 45g each) of instant rice vermicelli noodles
- 200g mangetout
- 200g baby sweetcorn
- 1 red pepper, deseeded and sliced
- 1 tablespoon extra virgin olive oil
- 1 tablespoon reduced salt soy sauce

Both teriyaki and soy sauce contain salt. In most of my recipes I use ordinary soy sauce as there is no salt added elsewhere in the dish (and I assume you are following my rules about no processed food! Therefore some salt is essential). However, this dish uses both teriyaki and soy sauce, so try to go for the low-salt variety if possible.

1. Rub the tuna steaks with the teriyaki sauce and garlic granules and set aside to marinate for 1 hour in the fridge.

2. Put the noodles in a large heatproof bowl and set aside. Pop the kettle on so you are ready to cook the noodles.

3. Heat a griddle pan or non-stick frying pan until very hot. Add the marinated tuna steaks and sear them until cooked to your liking (some people like their tuna rare; I prefer it cooked right through – the choice is yours. Check their doneness by cutting them open in the middle with a sharp knife).

4. Meanwhile, in a large non-stick frying pan or wok, stir-fry the vegetables for 3 minutes with the olive oil, then add the soy sauce and cook for another 1–2 minutes.

5. While the veggies and tuna are cooking, pour the boiling water over the noodles until they're covered, and leave for 2–3 minutes to cook.

6. Transfer the tuna steaks, once cooked to your liking, to a plate to rest, covered with foil.

7. Once the veggies are ready, drain the noodles and add them to the pan with the veg. Combine thoroughly and serve in four bowls, topping each serving with a rested tuna steak.

LIGHT

GINGER FISH WITH STIR-FRIED VEGGIES

SERVES 4

600g white fish fillets (cod, haddock or hoki), defrosted if using frozen fillets, and cut into large chunks
180g ribbon rice noodles
2 teaspoons sesame oil
4 spring onions, finely chopped
2 green peppers, deseeded and thinly sliced
1 red pepper, deseeded and thinly sliced
2cm piece of fresh root ginger, peeled and grated
120g watercress

FOR THE MARINADE:
2 garlic cloves, peeled and crushed
½ teaspoon chilli powder
2 tablespoons soy sauce
1 tablespoon Chinese rice wine (or white wine vinegar)
2 teaspoons sesame seeds
2 teaspoons sesame oil

Buy whatever fish is on offer and enjoy this Asian twist for fish. Fresh ginger is great for digestion, the fish is high in protein and you are getting a lot of nutrients from your quick, stir-fried veggies. Delicious!

1. Combine all the marinade ingredients in a large bowl, then add the fish chunks and swish them around. Set aside to marinate for 20 minutes.

2. Meanwhile, cook the ribbon rice noodles according to the packet instructions, then drain. Set aside.

3. Heat the sesame oil in a wok over a high heat. Drain the fish (reserving the marinade), add it to the wok and stir-fry for 1 minute, stirring continuously but gently so that you don't break up the chunks of fish.

4. Add the chopped spring onions, peppers and grated ginger and stir-fry for 2 minutes.

5. Finally, add the reserved marinade and simmer for 2–3 minutes, until the fish is cooked through and the sauce has thickened slightly.

6. Remove from the heat, fold in the watercress, and serve the stir-fry on a bed of the rice noodles.

ACTIVE

HEALTHY FISH PIE

SERVES 4

200g undyed smoked haddock fillets
200g salmon fillets
150ml skimmed milk
freshly ground black pepper, to taste
4 tablespoons extra virgin olive oil
1 medium onion, finely chopped
1 large leek, washed, trimmed and chopped
1 teaspoon ground cumin
2 tablespoons cornflour
6 tablespoons cold water
100g frozen sweetcorn, thawed
100g frozen peas, thawed
2 medium free-range hard boiled eggs, chopped
a handful of fresh parsley, chopped
4 tablespoons cornflour

FOR THE POTATO TOPPING:

400g cooked potatoes, mashed (leftovers, or freshly made)
200g cooked parsnips, mashed
200ml skimmed milk
2 tablespoons extra virgin olive oil

This healthy version of a delicious family favourite is made with skimmed milk instead of cream and mashed parsnip for extra flavour and nutrients – comfort food at its best!

1. Preheat the oven to 180°C/gas mark 4.

2. Gently warm the mashed potato and parsnips for the topping, and add the skimmed milk and olive oil. Combine well and set aside.

3. Place the haddock and salmon fillets in a saucepan, add the skimmed milk and a little black pepper and bring to the boil. Reduce the heat and simmer gently for 3–4 minutes. Once cooked (be careful not to overcook the fish), drain the fish and set aside, reserving the milk.

4. Meanwhile, heat the olive oil in a medium-sized saucepan, then add the onion, leek and cumin and cook until the onion is soft. Add the reserved milk to the pan and stir over a low heat. Then, add the cornflour and water, and stir continuously until the mixture thickens.

5. Once thick, remove from the heat and add the flaked cooked haddock and salmon and the sweetcorn, peas, boiled eggs and parsley. Season well with black pepper and carefully bring the mixture together, trying not to break up the flakes of fish. Transfer the mixture into a 25 x 15 x 4cm-deep baking dish.

6. Spoon the mashed potato and parsnip gently over the fish mixture, spreading it evenly with the back of a fork.

7. Bake for 30 minutes until nicely browned, then remove from the oven and serve immediately.

FISH & PANCETTA WRAPS WITH BROCCOLI

SERVES 4

grated zest of 1 lemon
a handful of fresh parsley, chopped
4 tablespoons extra virgin olive oil
freshly ground black pepper, to taste
600g fresh cod fillets, skinless, cut into eight pieces
8 slices of pancetta
600g broccoli, cut into florets

Pancetta is Italian bacon that is cut very thin, meaning it's perfect for adding extra flavour to this dish without making it heavy.

1. Preheat the oven to 220°C/gas mark 7 and line a baking tray with greaseproof paper.

2. Mix the lemon zest with the chopped parsley and olive oil and season well with black pepper. Dip each piece of fish in the herby oil.

3. Wrap a slice of pancetta around each piece of fish and place them on the prepared baking tray.

4. Bake for 10–12 minutes, or until the fish has turned opaque and is cooked through.

5. Meanwhile, cook the broccoli florets in a pan of boiling water, covered, until tender.

6. Drain the broccoli, then divide it between four plates and serve each plate topped with two pancetta-wrapped fish pieces.

BAKED COD PROVENÇAL

SERVES 2

- 1 red pepper, deseeded and cut into quarters
- 1 yellow pepper, deseeded and cut into quarters
- 1 courgette, cut into large chunks
- 120g cherry tomatoes
- 30g pitted black olives
- 4 shallots, peeled and quartered
- 3 garlic cloves, peeled and sliced
- 2 tablespoons extra virgin olive oil
- 2 x 150g fresh cod fillets, skinless
- a handful of fresh dill, chopped
- freshly ground black pepper, to taste
- grated zest and juice of 2 unwaxed limes

If you can't find good fresh cod, you can use frozen pieces instead. This dish has a lovely Mediterranean feel to it and is a perfect dish even if you've never cooked fish before!

1. Preheat the oven to 200°C/gas mark 6.

2. Mix the chopped vegetables, tomatoes, olives, shallots, garlic and olive oil together in a large bowl. Scatter into a shallow baking dish and roast for 15 minutes.

3. Remove the dish from the oven and place the cod fillets on top of the veggies, then sprinkle the fish with the chopped dill, black pepper, lime zest and juice and a little drizzle of olive oil.

4. Bake for a further 8–10 minutes, until the cod is cooked through. Serve immediately.

Cut out all fizzy drinks, even diet drinks unless it's fizzy water.

ACTIVE

LIGHTER SMOKED HADDOCK CHOWDER

SERVES 2

1 onion, peeled and chopped
1 garlic clove, peeled and crushed
2 waxy potatoes, scrubbed and thinly sliced
500ml low-salt vegetable stock
2 undyed smoked haddock fillets (about 100g each), skinned and cut into chunks
418g can creamed corn
4 tablespoons skimmed milk, or to taste
freshly ground black pepper, to taste
a handful of fresh parsley, chopped

This dish is a flexible feast. It's filling when you are starving and then seems light when a light lunch is required. It must be magic!

1. Put the onion, garlic and potatoes in a large frying pan over a medium heat. Pour over the vegetable stock and simmer for about 8 minutes until the potatoes are soft, but still have a slight bite.

2. Add the chunks of smoked haddock, the creamed corn and half of the milk (if you prefer thinner chowder, add more milk). Season with a little black pepper.

3. Simmer gently for 5–7 minutes, until the haddock is cooked (it should flake easily when pressed with a fork).

4. Sprinkle over the parsley and serve.

Eating healthily will give you the energy to make the most of everything.

LIGHT

SUMMER ROAST SALMON

SERVES 4

400g green beans, trimmed
200g broccoli, cut into florets
200g asparagus spears, trimmed
2 unwaxed lemons
freshly ground black pepper, to taste
1 teaspoon chilli flakes
2 tablespoons extra virgin olive oil
30g black Greek olives, pitted
4 vines of cherry tomatoes, each with 5–8 tomatoes on
4 boneless fresh or defrosted frozen salmon fillets, skin on (about 100g each)

This is my favourite summer fish dish. The flavours are so fresh and tasty – the olives and chilli give the otherwise mild salmon a summery kick!

1. Preheat the oven to 200°C/gas mark 6.

2. Bring a large saucepan of water to the boil over a high heat and add the green beans, broccoli florets and asparagus spears. Simmer for 2 minutes to blanch the vegetables, then drain immediately. Return the vegetables to the pan and fill the pan with enough cold water to cover them. Add a couple of ice cubes, and leave to go cold, then drain again.

3. Place the blanched, drained vegetables in a large roasting pan, squeeze over the juice of one lemon and season with black pepper and the chilli flakes. Drizzle with the olive oil, then scatter over the olives and place the vines of tomatoes on top.

4. Lay the salmon fillets, skin-side down, on top of the vegetables and squeeze over the juice from the second lemon. Add both the lemon skins to the pan. Roast in the centre of the oven for 20 minutes. Remove the lemon skins before serving.

The Bikini Promise is all about getting healthy – weight loss is a very happy side effect of that.

MINT & CUCUMBER COD SALAD

SERVES 4

½kg fresh cod fillet, cut from the thick end, skin removed and cut into four pieces
juice of ½ lemon
½ cucumber, washed and diced
½ small iceberg lettuce, washed and shredded
a small handful mint leaves, freshly chopped
a small handful of parsley, freshly chopped
freshly ground black pepper, to taste

FOR THE FRENCH DRESSING:
6 tablespoons light olive oil
2 tablespoons white wine vinegar
freshly ground black pepper, to taste
½ teaspoon wholegrain mustard
½ teaspoon soft dark brown sugar

FOR THE GARNISH:
25–50g cooked, peeled prawns
lemon wedges
sprigs of mint
green salad, to serve

Serve this gorgeous fresh summer salad with a small helping of new potatoes and a mixed salad.

1. Drizzle the fish with the lemon juice. Place in a large pan with a little water and a tight-fitting lid and poach over a medium heat until just cooked. (The flakes will look milky white and fall apart easily when the fish is cooked.) Remove the fish from the pan and leave to cool.

2. Mix together the diced cucumber, shredded lettuce, chopped mint and parsley in a large salad bowl.

3. Remove any bones from the fish and gently flake the flesh, then add it to the salad.

4. Mix all the French dressing ingredients together in a bowl and pour over the salad, taking care not to break up the fish flakes too much. Pile the mixture into four individual dishes and season with black pepper. Decorate with prawns, lemon wedges and sprigs of mint to serve.

TREAT AND EAT

TREAT & EAT

So here's the thing with treats. If you are on a diet, that means that at some stage, you will have to get off that diet. So, probably while on your diet, you would not be 'allowed' treats. (How awful!)

As someone who takes healthy eating very seriously, indeed to me it is a life-or-death choice rather than a lifestyle choice, I completely understand how important treats are. We all need a treat every now and then, and to deny ourselves these treats forever will eventually backfire (possibly when you and I dive headfirst into a huge chocolate gateaux!). However, by making the Bikini Promise, you are committing to eating for good health, and as you now know, weight loss is a fabulous side effect of that. Eating for good health has to be a lifelong commitment, and I hope my recipes prove to you that it is totally possible. So in that spirit, I have added this special chapter for you of Treats to Eat! Now, you must not eat these every day, and you must not eat anyone else's portion! These desserts are better than any shop-bought puds, and you are still eating clean as they do not contain chemicals, so in that respect they are guilt free. However, some do contain sugar and a bit of butter.

The thing to keep in mind is perspective. Eating one small bowl of Plum and Blackberry Crumble (my personal favourite) does not mean you have blown your diet. It **does not** mean you have to eat the whole thing. It simply means that you fancied something sweet or there was an occasion when everyone deserved a treat. It simply means that one piece isn't going to ruin your healthy eating plan forever; in fact, it is probably good for your soul! It simply means that tomorrow you take it easy with three **Light** meals instead of two **Light** and one **Active**. It simply means that you go for a slightly longer walk.

So, with that in mind my friends, enjoy!

PLUM & BLACKBERRY CRUMBLE

SERVES 4–6

light olive oil, for greasing
1 Bramley cooking apple, peeled, cored and roughly chopped
1kg dark red plums, stoned and halved
40g demerara sugar
150g fresh blackberries
1 cinnamon stick
100g rolled oats
100g plain flour
80g cold unsalted butter, cubed

Who doesn't love a crumble? A small serving of this crumble, packed with healthy and delicious dark red plums and fresh blackberries, makes for a healthy and gorgeous treat. Delicious!

1. Preheat the oven to 190°C/gas mark 5 and lightly grease a 25 x 17cm ovenproof dish using light olive oil on a piece of kitchen paper.

2. Place the apple, plums, 1 tablespoon of the sugar, 300ml of cold water and the blackberries in a large saucepan. Bring to the boil and add the cinnamon stick. Simmer, stirring occasionally, for 15–20 minutes, until thickened and reduced by half.

3. Meanwhile, in a large mixing bowl, mix the oats with the flour and remaining sugar. Rub the butter into the oat and flour mixture with your fingertips, until the mixture resembles breadcrumbs.

4. Pour the plum and apple mixture into the prepared dish, removing the cinnamon stick. Top with the crumble mixture and bake for 25–30 minutes, until the top is golden brown.

APPLE PIE SOUFFLÉ

SERVES 4

3 large free-range eggs, at room temperature, separated
100g caster sugar, plus an extra 20g
½ teaspoon vanilla extract
1 large Bramley cooking apple, peeled, cored and roughly chopped (other varieties of sharp apples, such as Cox or Granny Smith are also fine)
a pinch of ground cinnamon
1 tablespoon apple juice (optional)
small knob of butter
icing sugar, for dusting

The natural sweetness of the apple works perfectly with a hint of cinnamon to make a delicious, light dessert.

For this recipe you will need a frying pan that can go in the oven.

1. Preheat the oven to 180°C/gas mark 4.

2. Place the egg yolks and whites in separate bowls, ensuring the egg white bowl is spotlessly clean and grease free, and add 50g of the sugar to one bowl, and 50g to the other.

3. Add the vanilla extract to the egg yolks and whisk until the mixture forms a creamy, thick foam.

4. Whisk the egg whites until they form stiff peaks. Gently fold the egg yolks and whites together using a rubber spatula, being careful not to lose too much air from the mixture.

5. Put the chopped apple into a small non-metallic bowl with the remaining 20g sugar, cinnamon and a tablespoon of water or apple juice, cover with clingfilm, and cook in the microwave for about 2 minutes, until softened.

6. Melt the butter in an ovenproof frying pan over a medium heat until melted and sizzling, then pour in the soufflé mix and bake in the oven for 10 minutes, or until cooked and golden. Remove from the oven, sift a little icing sugar over the top, then pile the cooked apple in the middle and serve immediately, straight from the pan. Delicious!

GLUTEN-FREE CARROT CAKE

MAKES 12 SLICES

150g unsalted butter, at room temperature
150g caster sugar
3 free-range eggs, lightly beaten
75ml light olive oil
200g ground almonds
½ teaspoon ground nutmeg
½ teaspoon ground cinnamon
200g mixture of grated raw carrots, parsnip and beetroot
50g raisins
30g walnuts, chopped

FOR THE PASSION FRUIT TOPPING:
2 tablespoons passion fruit pulp (from approx. 1 passion fruit)
80g icing sugar

Using ground almonds instead of wheat flour means that this cake is perfect for anyone with a gluten allergy and also perfect as a non-stodgy treat for us all!

1. Preheat the oven to 200°C/gas mark 6, and line a 23cm round cake tin with baking parchment.

2. Beat the butter with the sugar in a large mixing bowl until pale and fluffy.

3. In a separate jug, whisk the 3 eggs with a fork and then add the beaten eggs bit by bit to the fat and sugar mixture, beating well after each addition before adding the next one.

4. Slowly add the light olive oil in a steady stream and mix lightly, then fold in the ground almonds and spices.

5. Finally, fold in the grated vegetables, raisins and chopped walnuts.

6. Pour the mixture into the prepared cake tin and bake for 40–45 minutes, or until the top has risen and is golden brown, and a skewer inserted into the centre comes out with no raw mixture stuck to it. If the cake starts to darken too quickly then cover the tin with foil.

7. Remove from the oven and allow to cool for 10 minutes before removing from the tin.

8. Meanwhile, mix the passion fruit pulp and the icing sugar together to make a runny sauce. Once the cake is cool, pour the passion fruit topping over the cake, letting it dribble down

CHOCOLATE BEANY CAKE

MAKES 12 SLICES

So 1 slice is a lovely treat – no need for any more!

- 400g can cannellini beans, drained and rinsed
- 5 large free-range eggs
- 3 tablespoons vegetable oil
- 3 tablespoons applesauce
- 400g caster sugar
- 1 tablespoon vanilla extract
- 6 tablespoons cocoa powder, sifted
- 1 teaspoon baking powder

This moist, rich chocolate cake has a very surprising ingredient: cannellini beans. The beans make it rich in fibre and protein, but lower in carbohydrates than if the cake was made with flour. You might find it hard to believe, but the cake always turns out great, and it's really easy to make.

The recipe calls for applesauce, which I make by peeling and chopping an apple (any kind of eating apple) into small chunks, and popping them in the microwave for 2 minutes until soft and squishy.

1. Preheat the oven to 170°C/gas mark 4 and line an 20cm round cake tin with baking parchment.

2. Place the drained cannellini beans in the bowl of a food-processor with two of the eggs and pulse until the mixture resembles a smooth cream. This may take a while – you want to ensure that no lumps remain.

3. Add the oil, applesauce, sugar and vanilla to the food-processor and beat for a few minutes.

4. Add the remaining eggs, cocoa and baking powder to the mixture and beat again for a further couple of minutes to ensure there are no lumps.

5. Pour the mixture into the prepared cake tin and bake for 40–45 minutes lightly covered with foil, checking if the cake is cooked by inserting a skewer in the middle and checking it comes out clean.

6. Cool on a wire rack before serving.

LOW-FAT CHOCCY & SUNFLOWER SEED BROWNIES

MAKES 16 BROWNIES

75g cocoa powder, sifted
130g caster sugar
25g sunflower seeds
2 tablespoons light olive oil, plus extra for greasing
175g apples, peeled and grated
1 free-range egg, plus 2 egg whites
1 teaspoon vanilla extract
75g wholemeal plain flour, sifted
½ teaspoon baking powder

This is a lower-fat version of the classic chocolate brownie. On the Bikini Promise, one piece is a treat to feed your soul!

1. Preheat the oven to 180°C/gas mark 4 and grease and line a 20cm square cake tin with baking parchment.

2. Put the cocoa, sugar and sunflower seeds in a large mixing bowl.

3. In a jug, whisk together the olive oil, grated apple, egg, egg whites and vanilla extract.

4. Stir the egg and apple mixture into the cocoa mixture, then gently fold in the flour and baking powder.

5. Spoon the mixture into the prepared tin and gently level the surface.

6. Bake for 15 minutes, or until the edges are firm and a skewer inserted into the centre comes out fairly clean. Remove from the oven and leave to cool in the tin for 5 minutes, then transfer to a wire rack to cool completely, before cutting into 16 pieces.

We all need a treat every now and then and to deny ourselves will eventually backfire.

MINI PEAR CRUMBLES

SERVES 4

4 firm pears, peeled, cored and chopped
1 teaspoon ground ginger
1 teaspoon ground cinnamon
2 tablespoons runny honey
juice of 1 lemon
10 ginger nut biscuits
30g rolled oats
2 tablespoons plain wholewheat flour
40g cold unsalted butter, cubed
low-fat crème fraîche, to serve

By serving this delicious pud in individual separate ramekins, you can control portion sizes perfectly.

1. Preheat the oven to 180°C/gas mark 4.

2. Place the chopped pears, ginger, cinnamon, honey and lemon juice and 3 tablespoons of water in a saucepan over a medium heat. Cook for about 10 minutes, stirring occasionally, until the pears are soft. Remove from the heat and set aside.

3. Place the ginger nut biscuits in a food-processor and pulse until roughly chopped, or crush them in a plastic sandwich bag with a rolling pin. Transfer to a mixing bowl and stir in the oats and flour.

4. Rub the cold butter into the biscuit, oat and flour mixture with your fingertips until a crumb-like texture forms. Divide the cooked pears between four 250ml ovenproof ramekins and top with the crumble mixture.

5. Bake for 15 minutes, or until the tops are browned, and serve with low-fat crème fraîche.

STRAWBERRIES & CREAM POWDER PUFFS

MAKES 8 PUFFS

light olive oil, for greasing
2 free-range eggs
4 tablespoons caster sugar
8 tablespoons plain flour
icing sugar, for dusting
low-fat crème fraîche and fresh strawberries, to serve

Light, melt-in-the-mouth delights that are low in fat and make the most deliciously tasty treat.

1. Preheat the oven to 180°C/gas mark 4 and grease eight holes of a 12-hole muffin tray with a little light olive oil on a piece of kitchen paper.

2. Whisk the eggs with the sugar, using a handheld electric whisk, for at least 5 minutes, until the mixture doubles in size and becomes very pale.

3. Sift the flour over the egg mixture and fold it in gently, using a large metal spoon (be careful not to overmix).

4. Drop rounded tablespoons of the mixture into the greased holes in the muffin tray.

5. Cook for 6–8 minutes, or until they are springy to the touch, then remove from the oven and leave to cool on a wire rack. Dust with icing sugar and serve with a dollop of low-fat crème fraîche and some sweet strawberries.

RED BERRY FILO TARTS

MAKES 8 TARTS

3 tablespoons light olive oil
150g fresh strawberries, hulled and halved
200g fresh mixed summer fruit (such as raspberries and blueberries)
2 tablespoons runny honey
2 tablespoons sunflower seeds
8 sheets filo pastry
icing sugar, for dusting
low-fat crème fraîche, to serve
fresh mint leaves, to serve

Filo pastry keeps this dessert lovely and light with fresh fruit and a little honey keeping it natural.

1. Preheat the oven to 180°C/gas mark 4. Grease eight holes of a 12-hole muffin tray with a little light olive oil, using a piece of kitchen paper.

2. In a large bowl, mix together the berries, honey and sunflower seeds. Set aside.

3. Lay the filo sheets on top of each other and cut the stack into eight squares. Take one of the eight stacks and brush each square of filo with olive oil. Layer the squares at different angles in one of the greased holes of the muffin tin, pushing the filo down into the hole, then continue with the remaining stacks, layering them into the remaining holes, until you have used all the stacks.

4. Divide the berry mixture between the filo cases and bake for 15 minutes, or until golden brown.

5. Dust each tart with a little icing sugar and serve with a dollop of low-fat crème fraîche and some fresh mint leaves.

SUMMER FRUIT COMPOTE

SERVES 4–6

200g punnet strawberries, hulled
200g punnet cherries, stoned
8 plums, stoned and cut into wedges
2 tablespoons runny honey
1 teaspoon ground cinnamon
2 star anise

This is a wonderful all-rounder; suitable for dessert with low-fat Greek yogurt, or great with porridge for breakfast. Cherries can be expensive when out of season, so if they're not in season, swap them for blackberries.

1. Preheat the oven to 200°C/gas mark 6.

2. Rinse the strawberries, cherries and plums and place in a roasting tray. Drizzle with the honey, sprinkle with cinnamon and add the star anise.

3. Roast the fruit for 25 minutes, until the fruit has softened. Eat warm or cold. Store in the fridge in an airtight container for up to three days.

SUMMER FRUIT & ALMOND FLATBREAD

MAKES 10 FLATBREADS

FOR THE FLATBREADS:
500g self-raising flour, plus extra for dusting
1 teaspoon baking powder
500g fat-free natural yogurt

FOR THE FRUIT TOPPING:
125g fresh blueberries
125g fresh raspberries
400g can apricots in juice, drained and chopped (pop the juice in the fridge and use for a smoothie later)
150g low-fat crème fraîche
2 tablespoons flaked almonds, toasted
a sprinkle of ground cinnamon and caster sugar, combined, to serve

This takes a little time to make because of the flatbread, but it is totally worth the effort. Once nibbled... often repeated!

1. To make the flatbreads, add all the flatbread ingredients to a bowl and bring them together, either using a stand mixer fitted with a dough hook or by mixing with a fork.

2. Knead the dough using the stand mixer or, if making by hand, tip the dough out onto a clean, lightly floured work surface and knead for 2–3 minutes.

3. Pop the dough into a flour-dusted bowl, cover with clingfilm and set aside while you prepare for the next stage.

4. Dust a clean work surface and rolling pin with flour, then divide the dough into 10 equal-sized pieces, roughly the size of a golf ball. Use the palms of your hands to flatten the dough, then roll out each piece until it is the thickness of a £1 coin.

5. Cook the flatbreads, one at a time, on a dry griddle pan (meaning no oil) or a dry frying pan for a couple of minutes on each side. Alternatively, bake in the oven (preheated to 200°C/gas mark 6) for 10 minutes.

6. While the flatbreads are cooking, mix together the blueberries, raspberries and apricots in a saucepan, and heat through over a low heat for 4–5 minutes.

7. When the flatbreads are cooked, spread each one with the warmed fruit, topped with a dollop of low-fat crème fraîche, the toasted almonds and a sprinkling of the cinnamon and sugar mixture. Serve immediately.

GREEN GODDESS SMOOTHIE

SERVES 2

½ avocado, pitted and peeled
a handful of spinach
a handful of kale
50g frozen pineapple chunks
10cm piece of cucumber
300ml cold water

The trick with all healthy smoothies is to get the balance right between fruit and veggies. You need a little fruit to bring the sweetness, but not so much that you overload on sugar. This is energy in a glass!

Pop all the ingredients into a food-processor or smoothie maker with 300ml cold water and blitz until smooth.

RED JUICY LUCY

SERVES 2

1 apple peeled, cored and roughly chopped
50g fresh blueberries
2cm piece of fresh root ginger, peeled and grated
2 small, raw beetroot, peeled
300ml cold water

Pop all the ingredients into a food-processor or smoothie maker with 300ml cold water and blitz until smooth.

VITAMIN BOOSTER

SERVES 2

1 large carrot peeled
1 large orange, peeled, pith removed and segmented
2 sticks celery
50g frozen mango chunks
300ml cold water

Pop all the ingredients into a food-processor or smoothie maker with 300ml cold water and blitz until smooth.

HEART-HEALTHY POMEGRANATE PUNCH

MAKES 1 LITRE

500ml red wine
500ml unsweetened pomegranate juice
2 teaspoons runny honey
1 orange, thinly sliced
5 cloves
seeds of 1 vanilla pod

Pomegranates are super heart healthy. Anything with a natural deep red colour contains lots of antioxidants and should be eaten, or drank, as often as possible. This is delicious served warm or cold.

1. Place a medium-sized saucepan over a low heat and add the red wine, pomegranate juice, honey, orange slices, cloves and vanilla seeds.

2. Simmer gently for 5 minutes, then strain through a sieve and serve in heatproof glasses.

Silence your inner critic and learn to love your body! Once you love your body, you are more likely to nourish it properly.

INDEX

The Bikini Promise is dedicated to my mum who taught me that confidence is the most attractive asset and who, in my eyes, was the most beautiful pin-up girl in the world. xxx

Huge, enormous thanks go to everyone who has helped me pull this book together in superfast time.

Sam and Jess, thank you for everything. Just EVERYTHING! You both know what you mean to me.

Sue Walton at ITV for letting me be me, and do what I've needed to do! This would not have been possible without you believing in me.

Lorraine Kelly for her lovely friendship, kindness and great support and generosity on screen.

Maxine Jones for being my very energetic partner in crime!

Shirley Patton for 'paving the way' in the most determined yet gentle way possible.

Judith Hannam and the whole team at Kyle Books for their constant professionalism and passion.

Nicky Johnston, Dogan Halil and Clare Winfield for the beautiful photography.

And, of course, always thanks to my Mr Bee and Little Bees for being mine!

Heartfelt thank to you all. xxx

First published in Great Britain in 2015, to accompany the ITV television show Lorraine, by Kyle Books, an imprint of Kyle Cathie Ltd.
192–198 Vauxhall Bridge Road
London SW1V 1DX
general.enquiries@kylebooks.com
www.kylebooks.com

10 9 8 7 6 5 4 3 2 1

ISBN 978 0 85783 311 2

Editor: Judith Hannam
Editorial assistant: Hannah Coughlin
Designer: Caroline Clark
Photographers: Clare Winfield, Nicky Johnston, Dogan Halil
Prop stylist: Wei Tang
Food stylist: Mima Sinclair
Production: Gemma John and Nic Jones

A Cataloguing in Publication record for this title is available from the British Library.

Colour reproduction by ALTA London.
Printed and bound in Spain by Indice Arts Gràfiques.

Thank you to Spring Studios, www.springstudios.com.